D1369744

PAST AND PRESENT CAUSES
IN GEOLOGY

Frontispiece: Portrait of Lucien Cayeux. Reproduced from *Institut de France—Académie des Sciences, Paris, Notices et Discours,* volume 2 (1937-1948), 1949, p. 607, with permission from the *Institut de France.*

PAST AND PRESENT CAUSES IN GEOLOGY

by
LUCIEN CAYEUX

translated and edited by
ALBERT V. CAROZZI
Professor of Geology, University of Illinois

HAFNER PUBLISHING COMPANY
New York
1971

Copyright © 1971
Hafner Publishing Company, Inc.

Library
I.U.P.
Indiana, Pa.

This translation is published by special permission of
the publishers of the original 1941 French edition:

Masson & Cie, Éditeurs
120 Boulevard Saint-Germain
Paris VI, France

552.5   C317p
c. 1

Published by
HAFNER PUBLISHING COMPANY, INC.
866 Third Avenue
New York, N.Y. 10022

Library of Congress Catalog Card Number: 76-147276

All rights reserved. No part of this book may be
reproduced or transmitted in any form or by any means,
electronic or mechanical, including photocopying,
recording or by any information storage and retrieval
system, without permission in writing from the Publisher.

Printed in U.S.A. by

Grammatici certant et
adhuc sub judice lis est.

Horatius, *Ars Poetica*, 78

PREFACE

Whenever the late Paul D. Krynine introduced himself—facetiously as usual—he would say: "I am the second petrographer in the world". By these words he meant that Lucien Cayeux, whom he deeply admired, was unquestionably the first.

Cayeux wrote this little volume partially to replace his final years of lecturing which were cancelled by a politically imposed early retirement. It contains his synthetical views on one of the most critical aspects of geological thinking: do past and present causes really exist? Cayeux's discussion is based on a series of well-documented and striking examples of cementation, dolomitization, recrystallization, replacement and reworking among phosphorites, iron ores, cherts and carbonates. These examples, which he interpreted to be essentially of *submarine origin* and *penecontemporaneous with sedimentation*, appear as remarkable anticipations in the light of modern sedimentological investigations.

This last work of Cayeux has remained little known after the waves of sharp criticisms that it stirred up in 1949, a few years after his death. It is an unusually difficult volume to understand because it assumes that the reader is completely familiar with the entire and enormous contribution of Cayeux which is continuously and briefly referred to.

My task, besides translating and editing the original text, has been to replace Cayeux's page quotations by their fully translated equivalents, often accompanied by illustrations and by additional material, condensed or not, in order to provide the reader with the necessary documents for a better understanding of the synthesis. The progress of geological knowledge since 1941 has confirmed or discredited some of the predictions of Cayeux. Therefore, comments and references have been inserted between square brackets in the original text at appropriate places. It is my hope to have achieved a self-sufficient unit associating Cayeux's observations, process of reasoning and conclusions.

The volume, because of its provocative title *"Causes anciennes et causes actuelles en géologie"*, has been, to a large extent, considered as a refutation of the principle of uniformity in geology and rather quickly disposed of in such terms. It is the purpose of the Editor's Introduction to show that such a dismissal is really unwarranted. Cayeux's book is in my opinion a fascinating, yet little known attempt, to show the intriguing results of the variations of the effects of a pool of permanent causes in which "ancient" and "present" causes are associated at all times, but whose effects are only the consequences of the circumstances under which these permanent causes can act.

For instance, nowhere did I see so clearly "ancient" causes in full activity *today* as in the immense delta of the Amazon. In this incredibly flat and forever green landscape through which it is said that one fifth of the total freshwater of the world finds its outlet toward the sea, many fundamental concepts of geology seem to become confused, as if vanishing in the steaming haze of the equator. This is true for the limit between land and sea, between marine and freshwater and even for the very banks of the river, all of which are but fleeting situations regulated by the complex interplay of stream flow and tides. Even more difficult to grasp is the reality of a seaward slope when during half of the time the enormous mass of brownish water moves upstream for hundreds of miles as a temporary embayment of the ocean.

Watching the Amazon delta I had the overwhelming feeling of being brought back to the time of the Pennsylvanian cyclothems of central North America. But when traveling upstream, the *past world* of the Pennsylvanian coal-bearing swamps grades into the *present world* of earthquakes and orogeny of the Andes. Therefore past and present causes are indeed part of a single and grandiose scheme forever active, and I hope to convince the reader that Lucien Cayeux thought likewise.

During this short incursion into the controversial world of fundamental geological principles, I needed, as for a typical expedition up the Amazon river, many devoted helpers: indispensable guides such as the late and much regretted Harold R. Wanless and my dear friend George W. White; the watchful scouts such as Mrs. Harriet W. Smith, Geology Librarian, Harry Lubrecht and Jacques Strauss of Hafner Publishing Company; and most of all the ever present spirit of the forest which insures that I avoid the pitfalls of the "terra caída" or do not become lost in the "igapó": my wife.

Belém, Pará   A. V. Carozzi
Urbana, Illinois
September 1970

CONTENTS

EDITOR'S INTRODUCTION

Lucien Cayeux, at the end of an unusually productive career—almost fifty years—in the microscopic investigation of the entire spectrum of sedimentary rocks, presents in this book a viewpoint which has been generally considered as a refutation of the principle of uniformity.

According to his two critics, Robert Laffitte (1949) and Martin G. Rutten (1949), Cayeux is supposed to be of the opinion that the formation of certain past marine sediments can only be explained by the operation of mysterious ancient causes, and that the latter are totally non-existent today, having been replaced by an entirely different set of present causes. R. Hooykaas (1963, pp. 3-4, 52-56), after a long discussion of Cayeux's ideas where he essentially agreed with the criticism of Laffitte and Rutten, assumes that Cayeux's concept could be considered approximately as follows: "the causes of some geological changes of the past *differ in kind from those now in operation but are not more violent*." That is, in former periods of the earth's history forces of another kind ("ancient causes") were operating, but they were not of a more catastrophic character than those in action now.

This assumed doubt about the validity of uniformitarianism, an attitude in flagrant opposition to the permanency of the fundamental laws of physics, seems rather extreme to be adopted by such an experienced geologist as Cayeux. This position could not even be considered as hasty or senile taken near the end of his career, since the first expression of it may be found in his doctoral dissertation, dated 1897. It will reappear as leitmotif in some of the conclusions of his voluminous monographs on the chalk, the iron ores, the siliceous rocks, the carbonates and the phosphates. Since there is still today no question about the validity of the fully documented observations that he presented, it seems to me that Cayeux's critics have misunderstood his message.

While undertaking the translation of this volume I had to take a very careful look at the wording of Cayeux's statements and it became apparent that they contain many nuances and are consequently not so categorical as they seem to be at first glance.

I shall quote here, in their order of presentation by Cayeux, some of his major statements and conclusions followed by a few appropriate comments.

". . . present processes are not always capable of explaining past events . . ." (p. 8) He says *not always* (French: *pas toujours*), therefore, present processes are able, in some cases, to explain past events.

". . . I am not going to challenge point by point the doctrine of Present Causes whose great effectiveness should not be disputed. Yet, I have been led . . . to the conclusion that many Ancient causes do not have equivalents among Present causes . . ." (p. 8) Here, the word *many* is used (French: *bien des*), consequently, not all ancient causes have no equivalents because they have disappeared. Logically, one can assume that some ancient causes must have present equivalents.

". . . present processes are far from being the truthful image of past ones . . ." (p. 23) This again does not imply that present processes have replaced ancient ones, but that for certain reasons, some effects clearly displayed in ancient sediments have become almost imperceptible at present.

". . . this is another instance showing that the environmental conditions of ancient seas are very often different from those of present seas . . ." (p. 35) Notice the use of "very often" (French: *très souvent*) and not *always* different. In other words, some ancient seas had environmental conditions similar to those of present ones.

". . . some causes which play a fundamental role in the formation of ancient sediments do not participate at all in the generation of present-day deposits." (p. 73) Two words should be stressed in this statement, first, *some* ancient causes, not all of them, do not participate in the deposition of present sediments; second, *do not participate* (French:

n'interviennent pas), in other words, their effects are not detectable. These causes are essentially inactive, but have not disappeared having been replaced by entirely different ones.

". . . the present epoch is characterized by the inactivity of a series of processes which played a great role in the formation of sediments during the geological past." (p. 75) Cayeux says *inactivity* (French: *repos*), not *absence* of a series of processes at present. In other words, these processes are potentially present, but their effects are difficult to detect or geographically restricted, but the processes themselves have not disappeared and been replaced by others.

". . . therefore, the data obtained from the analysis of Past causes and of their effects should not be neglected—if it were only for the purpose of stating problems, and of contributing to establish a research program fulfilling the needs of geology—on the day when oceanographical exploration will start anew and on a much larger scale than in the past." (p. 78) If the data afforded by rocks formed through the action of "past" causes should be taken into consideration for establishing some of the goals of modern oceanography, this implies that some present marine environments might well, upon extensive investigation, show these "past" causes locally active. Indeed, recent investigations have confirmed the coexistence of "past" and "present" causes today, their difference being only a matter of geographic extent and nature of effects as suggested by M.G. Rutten (1949).

". . . In the study of the sedimentary formations of the earth's crust, it is necessary to take into account ancient causes besides present causes, if one wishes to use all the factors capable of providing a complete understanding of such formations." (p. 79) Cayeux says that ancient causes should be considered *besides* (French: *à côté*) present causes, not *in the place of*. He does not mean that ancient sediments were produced under the influence of past causes which have ceased to exist at present, having been replaced by a new set of present causes; he says that in order to understand ancient sediments we should combine ancient causes with present causes.

Before drawing any final conclusions on Cayeux's thinking, some data should be given on the rocks he so carefully
investigated. The essentials of his observations pertain to the
chalk and its cherts, the oolitic iron ores and the phosphates.
In these deposits he repeatedly noticed the puzzling association of two conflicting sets of characters: one similar to those
of recent pelagic sediments deposited in mid-ocean, the other
indicating neritic conditions similar to recent near-shore
coastal deposits. For such environmental interpretations he
used extensively the results of the "Challenger" expedition
which in his time represented the basic background of
oceanography. To understand such an association he assumed
the effects of particular processes not active today. I should
stress that he remained silent about the factors regulating the
deposition of the other groups of ancient rocks, such as the
different types of shales, sandstones and even carbonates
associated with the deposits he studied. He remained equally
silent about the agents responsible for the deposition of the
thick clastic series which alternate with the chalk, the iron
ores and the phosphates throughout the geological column. I
am therefore entitled to assume that he found nothing
peculiar about them as compared to present sediments, hence
not all ancient deposits are different from present ones, only
some of them. In other words, the conclusion may be
reached that the past geological record not only displays
thick clastic series similar to present deposits, but also shows
the *simultaneous occurrence* of rocks which might claim
"ancient" and "recent" causes as their regulating factors.

This situation is perfectly understandable since the chalk,
the oolitic iron ores and the phosphates, as widespread as
they might have been in the past, were certainly not the only
kind of sediments being deposited over the entire earth at a
given time. Therefore, "ancient" and "present" causes were
associated at all times forming a pool of *permanent causes*. In
other words, throughout the geological column, the causes
(or the physical forces, such as gravity) have really never
changed, but during given periods the effects of certain
causes were largely predominant while the effects of others
were barely noticeable or restricted to certain areas; at other

periods the reverse would occur. Since the causes are permanent, these differences in their effects can only be the consequences of two different circumstances under which these forces or causes acted. Therefore, the "ancient" and "present" causes really mean ancient and present situations during which permanent causes led to different geological results, in this particular case different sediments.

If Cayeux's contribution is understood along these lines, and I think it should be, he becomes as uniformitarian as his critics. He has not only preceded them in some of their conclusions, such as the periodical occurrence of these two sets of circumstances, but has also anticipated, as we shall see later, the discovery of many types of present sediments which in localized areas obey "ancient" causes. Consequently his book is not a refutation of uniformitarianism, but an attempt to show the intriguing results of the variations of the effects of permanent causes. The question is now to understand the real nature of these two sets of circumstances and the intrinsic reasons for their periodical occurrence during geological time. This periodicity, long ago visualized by Hutton, was refuted by the rigid approach of Lyell but has recently been included by Laffitte and Rutten, among others, in the modern and enlarged definition of uniformitarianism (Hooykaas, *op. cit.* pp. 56-64).

Concerning the real nature of these two sets of circumstances, Cayeux made a miscalculation of the order of magnitude of the processes he was observing, mainly because of his great emphasis on petrographic studies under the microscope. This error of appreciation, as pointed out by Laffitte and Rutten, consisted in his tendency to exaggerate the importance of the disturbances or *ruptures of equilibrium* which he considered responsible for the puzzling and repeated alternations of "pelagic" and "neritic" sediments in the chalk, the oolitic iron ores and the phosphates. This association implied for him oscillations of the sea floor of an amplitude similar to the difference of depth existing today between oceanic bottoms covered with pelagic sediments and continental shelves overlain by neritic deposits. Cayeux however pointed out that he visualized these ruptures of equilibrium as nothing but regional disturbances, devoid of any influence on the areas located beyond their direct action: "Is it necessary to add that these ruptures of equilibrium do not have the magnitude and the generality of Cuvier's catastrophes?" (p. 75) This geographical restriction of the action of the past causes represented by their ruptures of equilibrium reinforces the point made above that sediments claiming "past" and "present" causes as their regulating factors coexisted in the geological past.

Whenever Cayeux observed the repeated alternations of "pelagic" and "neritic" conditions he assumed that the deposits he investigated represented *epochs of great instability of the sea floor*. On the contrary, the other periods would represent *times of stability*. In that respect Cayeux says: ". . . the present is in essence a period of great stability of the sea level and of the sea floor. Therefore, we are dealing with an exception in comparison with the geological periods taken as a whole . . ." (p. 75) [As pointed out below, the present is certainly exceptional but because of its postorogenic instability, Cayeux's incorrect assumption of stability resulted from his above-described miscalculation of the order of magnitude of the processes involved.] "Consequently it is only by means of the analysis of ancient sediments, and only through it, that we can reach an understanding of the ancient processes of the marine environment." (p. 77)

The two critics of Cayeux, Laffitte and Rutten, have presented new and essentially identical interpretations of these two sets of circumstances which summarize the present state of our knowledge and stressed that Cayeux's concept of stability and instability was erroneous. At the same time they explained the reasons for the periodical occurrence of such circumstances through geological time.

It is known today that all the deposits investigated by Cayeux: the chalk, the oolitic iron ores and the phosphates, belong to long periods of orogenic quietness, in other words to the so-called *periods of epeirogenic movements* which consist of gentle and slow oscillations. These periods are characterized by very extensive and shallow seas, bordered by low-elevation continental masses, often almost peneplained and therefore releasing very little clastic materials. Hence, the marine sedimentation was essentially pelagic and the slightest epeirogenic uplifting would have far-reaching consequences on the sedimentation, such as widespread ruptures of equilibrium and related reworking which generates detrital (pseudo-littoral) deposits, extensive supratidal dolomites, large-scale conditions of seepage refluxion through well-developed reef barriers and broad evaporitic lagoons in the middle of pelagic deposits. Naturally, in other areas which had escaped erosion and which must have been geographically restricted, other types of sediments similar to the present ones were deposited. But these types of sediments would represent an exception hardly affecting the general picture, which is essentially dominated by the great development of the effects related to the existence of extensive shallow seas surrounded by lowlands.

At other times, during the relatively short *periods of orogenic activity*, including the postorogenic times immediately following them—like the present—the earth was characterized by high continental reliefs undergoing active erosion, deep oceanic basins, narrow continental shelves receiving abundant clastic sedimentation, uplifted and drowned coastlines, almost no shallow seas, effects of glaciations. The resulting sedimentation is characterized at present by a strong contrast between pelagic deep-sea deposits and shallow clastic sediments, in the past by deep-sea siliceous or carbonate rocks and by thick clastics of flysch and molasse type. Naturally, in other areas which have escaped the rugged modern conditions and show a topography similar to the general physiography which prevailed during epeirogenic periods, one finds on a small scale sediments similar to those of these periods. Such is the case of the flat and almost invisible coast near the mouth of the Senegal (Laffitte, 1949), the restricted lagoons where supratidal dolomitization occurs in the Persian Gulf, in Florida, in the Bahamas and elsewhere (Friedman and Sanders, 1967; Illing, Wells and Taylor, 1965; Shinn, 1964;

Shinn, Ginsburg and Lloyd, 1965; Von der Borch, Rubin and Skinner, 1964), of the small-scale conditions of seepage refluxion through modern reefs (Adams and Rhodes, 1960; Deffeyes, Lucia and Weyl, 1965; Murray, 1969) and of the limited shoals where oolitization takes place in the Bahamas (Bathurst, 1968; Illing, 1954; Newell, Purdy and Imbrie, 1960) and along the southern coasts of the Mediterranean (Castany and Lucas, 1955; Hilmy, 1951; Lucas, 1955). However the present-day formation of oolites in the Gulf of Gabes (southern Tunisia) has been recently refuted (Fabricius, Berdau and Münnich, 1970).

Additional types of such deposits recalling closely those of the epeirogenic periods seem to be influenced more by local environmental similarities than by the general physiography. This is the case of the ferruginous pellets (goethite and chamosite) reported along the coasts of the Ivory Coast and Gabon, in the Malacca Strait, on the Sarawak and Guinea shelves, in the Niger and Orinoco-Paria deltas and in the Loch Etive in Scotland (Von Gaertner and Schellmann, 1965; Giresse, 1965; Leneuf, 1962; Porrenga, 1965 and 1967; Rohrlich, Price and Calvert, 1969). Similar considerations apply to the phosphatic nodules scattered off the coasts of California and Baja California, and along many other coastlines around the world (D'Anglejan, 1967; Dietz, Emery and Shepard, 1942; Mero, 1961; Sheldon, 1964), and finally to the incipient cherts forming today in the alkaline lakes of East Africa (Hay, 1968; Eugster, 1967; Peterson and Von der Borch, 1965).

However, all these deposits, in spite of their great intrinsic interest remain exceptions hardly affecting the present picture, which is essentially dominated by the great development of the effects related to the existence of deep ocean basins surrounded by high reliefs.

In essence, the two sets of circumstances just described express two general and distinct physiographic states of the earth corresponding respectively to long epeirogenic periods and to relatively short orogenic episodes, both being the direct manifestation of the periodical nature of the internal forces of the globe.

In conclusion, the observation of the present pattern of sedimentation in a world undergoing orogeny, or perhaps just emerging from an orogenic phase, demonstrates clearly that "present" and "ancient" causes are associated in a pool of permanent causes which give rise to a set of sediments typical of the present-day rugged face of the earth. Therefore, there is no opposition, at any time, between "ancient" and "present" causes. This is precisely the manner in which Cayeux's contribution should be interpreted and the reason why, in my opinion, it retains its outstanding value. Cayeux only stressed examples in which the permanent causes, acting on a different or "ancient" world produced sediments spectacularly different from those of today.

REFERENCES

ADAMS, J.E. and M.L. RHODES, Dolomitization by seepage refluxion: *Bull. Am. Assoc. Petroleum Geologists*, 1960, vol. 44, pp. 1912-1920.

ANGLEJAN, B.F.D', Origin of marine phosphorites off Baja California, Mexico: *Marine Geology*, 1967, vol. 5, pp. 15-44.

BATHURST, R.G.C., Precipitation of oöids and other aragonite fabrics in warm seas: *Recent Developments in Carbonate Sedimentology in Central Europe* (G. Müller and G.M. Friedman, editors), 1968, Springer Verlag New York Inc., pp. 1-10.

CASTANY, G. and G. LUCAS, Sur l'existence d'oolithes calcaires actuelles au large de l'île de Djerba (Sud-Tunisien): *C.R. Somm. Soc. Géol. France*, 1955, No. 12, pp. 229-232.

DEFFEYES, K.S., F. Jerry LUCIA and P.K. WEYL, Dolomitization of Recent and Plio-Pleistocene sediments by marine evaporite waters on Bonaire, Netherlands Antilles: *S.E.P.M. Spec. Publ. No. 13*, 1965, pp. 71-88.

DIETZ, R.S., K.O. EMERY and F.P. SHEPARD, Phosphorite deposits on the sea floor off Southern California: *Bull. Geol. Soc. America*, 1942, vol. 53, pp. 815-848.

EUGSTER, H.P., Hydrous sodium silicates from Lake Magadi, Kenya: precursors of bedded cherts: *Science*, 1967, vol. 157, No. 3793, pp. 1177-1180.

FABRICIUS, F.H., D. BERDAU and K.O. MUNNICH, Early Holocene oöids in modern littoral sands reworked from a coastal terrace, southern Tunisia: *Science*, 1970, vol. 169, No. 3947, pp. 757-760.

FRIEDMAN, G.M. and J.E. SANDERS, Origin and occurrence of dolostones: *Carbonate Rocks, Origin, Occurrence and Classification*, Developments in Sedimentology 9 A, (G.V. Chilingar, H.J. Bissell and R.W. Fairbridge, Editors), Amsterdam, Elsevier, 1967, pp. 267-348.

GAERTNER, H.R. Von and W. SCHELLMANN, Rezente Sedimente im Kuestenbereich der Halbinsel Kaloum, Guinea: *Mineral. Petrog. Mitt.*, 1965, vol. 10, pp. 349-367.

GIRESSE, P., Oolithes ferrugineuses en voie de formation au large du Cap Lopez (Gabon): *C.R. Acad. Sc. Paris*, 1965, vol. 260, pp. 2550-2552.

HAY, R.L., Chert and its sodium-silicate precursors in sodium-carbonate lakes of East Africa: *Beitr. Mineral. Petro. Dtsch.*, 1968, vol. 17, pp. 255-274.

HILMY, M.E., Beach sands of the Mediterranean coast of Egypt: *Jour. Sed. Petrology*, 1951, vol. 21, pp. 109-120.

HOOYKAAS, R., *The principle of uniformity in geology, biology and theology*: 1963, Leiden, E.J. Brill, 237 p.

ILLING, L.V., Bahaman calcareous sands: *Bull. Am. Assoc. Petrol. Geologists*, 1954, vol. 38, pp. 1-95.

ILLING, L.V., A.J. WELLS and J.C.M. TAYLOR, Penecontemporary dolomite in the Persian Gulf: *S.E.P.M. Spec. Publ. No. 13*, 1965, pp. 89-111.

LAFFITTE, R., Sédimentation et orogenèse: *Annales Hébert et Haug, Livre jubilaire Charles Jacob*, 1949, vol. 8, pp. 239-259.

LENEUF, N., Les pseudo-oolithes ferrugineuses des plages de Côte d'Ivoire: *C.R. Somm. Soc. Géol. France*, 1962, No. 5, pp. 145-146.

LUCAS, G., Oolithes marines actuelles et calcaires oolithiques récents sur le rivage africain de la Méditerranée orientale (Egypte et Sud Tunisien): *Bull. Stat. Océanogra. Salammbo (Tunisie)*, 1955, vol. 52, pp. 19-38.

MERO, J.L., Sea floor phosphorite: *California Div. Mines, Mineral Inf. Service*, 1961, vol. 14, No. 11, pp. 1-12.

MURRAY, R.C., Hydrology of South Bonaire, N.A.—A rock selective dolomitization model: *Jour. Sed. Petrology*, 1969, vol. 39, pp. 1007-1013.

NEWELL, N.D., E.G. PURDY and J. IMBRIE, Bahamian oölitic sands: *Jour. Geol.*, 1960, vol. 68, pp. 481-497.

PETERSON, M.N.A. and C.C. VON DER BORCH, Chert: modern inorganic deposition in a carbonate-precipitating locality: *Science*, 1965, vol. 149, No. 3691, pp. 1501-1503.

PORRENGA, D.H., Chamosite in Recent sediments of the Niger and Orinoco deltas: *Geologie en Mijnbouw*, 1965, vol. 44, pp. 400-403.

——————————, Glauconite and chamosite as depth indicators in the marine environment: *Marine Geology*, 1967, vol. 5, pp. 495-501.

ROHRLICH, V., N.B. PRICE and S.E. CALVERT, Chamosite in the Recent sediments of Loch Etive, Scotland: *Jour. Sed. Petrology*, 1969, vol. 39, pp. 624-631.

RUTTEN, M.G., Actualism in epeirogenetic oceans: *Geologie en Mijnbouw*, 1949, vol. 11, pp. 222-228.

SHELDON, R.P. Paleolatitudinal and paleogeographic distribution of phosphorite: *U.S. Geol. Surv. Prof. Paper* 501-C, 1964, pp. 106-113.

SHINN, E.A., Recent dolomite, Sugarloaf Key, Florida, *in* Guidebook for G.S.A. Field Trip No. 1, *South Florida Carbonate Sediments* (compiled by R.N. GINSBURG), 1964, pp. 62-67.

SHINN, E.A., R.N. GINSBURG and R.M. LLOYD, Recent supratidal dolomite from Andros Island, Bahamas: *S.E.P.M. Spec. Publ. No. 13*, 1965, pp. 112-123.

VON DER BORCH, C.C., M. RUBIN and B.J. SKINNER, Modern dolomite from South Australia: *Am. Jour. Sc.*, 1964, vol. 262, pp. 1116-1118.

PAST AND PRESENT CAUSES IN GEOLOGY

by

Lucien Cayeux

of the *Académie des Sciences*

As an expression of my deep gratitude, I dedicate this volume

1. To the memory of my teachers in geology:
    Jules Gosselet, Charles Barrois and
    Marcel Bertrand, members of the *Institut.*

2. To the *Collège de France*, the
    Ecole nationale supérieure des Mines,
    and to the *Institut national agronomique.*

L.C.

INTRODUCTION

During the past century, geology progressed under the influence of the theory of *Present Causes*, proposed and developed by Charles Lyell as a reaction against Cuvier's catastrophism. Lyell's *"Principles of Geology"*, which exerted a far-reaching and positive influence on the advancement of our science during the nineteenth century, are entirely based on the application of the following leading idea:

> *"Causes similar in kind and energy to those now acting have produced the former changes of the earth's surface."* [1]

as written by Charles Lyell.

Consequently, the study of ancient rocks must be preceded by that of present processes, this being the only rational method for unravelling the secret (8)* of the igneous and sedimentary rocks which build the earth's crust. In summary, this subject requires the study of the past in the light of the present. This is why the teaching of geology begins with the study of the last chapter of the earth's history, dealing with present-day processes.

One does not need to undertake elaborate investigations of the present economy of nature to become convinced that present processes are not always capable of explaining past events. For instance, it is well known that the earth has repeatedly undergone orogenic processes whereas, during modern times, no such manifestation has occurred.

I am not going to challenge point by point the doctrine of Present causes whose great effectiveness should not be

---

*For reference purposes, the page numbers of Cayeux's original text are retained in the English translation and are enclosed in parenthesis. Each page number refers to the material following it.

disputed. Yet, I have been led by my investigation of sedimentary rocks to the conclusion that *many Ancient causes*[2] *do not have any equivalents among Present causes*. The facts to be described below—among others that could be called upon in that respect—will allow me to prove this viewpoint. (9)

CHAPTER I

DATA PROVIDED BY SEDIMENTARY PHOSPHORITES AND OOLITIC IRON ORES

In the demonstration I shall now undertake and during which reference will be very often made to the original memoirs containing a wealth of pertinent data, *sedimentary phosphorites* and *oolitic iron ores* will play an important role. These two groups of deposits, of great economical importance, are characteristically excluded from the sediments being deposited at present. Therefore, they provide an argument of exceptional value for our viewpoint.

While the absence of oolitic iron ores among present deposits is unquestionable, it is not so for phosphorites. [For a discussion of Recent marine deposits of iron and phosphates, see Editor's Introduction.] On that subject and based on a general investigation not yet completely published, I shall only say that not a single *deposit* of phosphorite is known to be forming at present and that large scale deposition of that material is impossible today due to a fundamental reason. (10)

If I were to limit myself to this brief statement, I would have to avoid discussing a series of processes unknown at present and whose combined action is required for generating deposits of phosphorites and of oolitic iron ores. The picture afforded by these processes is, for the planned study, of such essential nature that I shall sketch it immediately.

I. DEPOSITS OF SEDIMENTARY PHOSPHORITES

While briefly investigating the field of sedimentary phosphorites I have observed, for the first time, processes which

1

unquestionably escape the law of Present causes. Actually,
chance had confronted me at the onset of my career with a
highly informative example, appearing as an accident of little
significance if it were unique, but presenting a fundamental
importance if the related process were to be subject to
repetition in the ancient seas.

The phosphatic chalk of the Paris Basin will provide us
with this particular example and the North African phosphorites with data for generalization. (11)

1. *Phosphatic chalk of the Paris Basin* [3]

The phosphatic chalk with *Belemnitella quadrata*, extensively quarried in the past in the *départements* of Pas-de-
Calais, Aisne, Somme and Oise, displays all the features of a
petrographic accident, developed in the very middle of the
Senonian white chalk in the central part of the Paris Basin. It
is a gray, coarse-grained and soft chalk, consisting essentially
of pinhead-sized granules of calcium phosphate, *interbedded
between two very fine-grained white chalks, and grading
laterally into a chalk as fine-grained as the above-mentioned
ones*.

This phosphatic chalk appears, on account of all its
features, so strikingly different from the enclosing chalks of
pelagic origin that my teacher J. Gosselet, after an investigation described in a series of short papers of great interest,
interpreted it as a littoral deposit. At first glance, this opinion
seems correct because it explains very well the conditions of
occurrence and the physical characteristics of the rock. The
changes undergone by the underlying chalk with *Micraster
cor anguinum*, such as perforations and erosion, as well as the
following features: occurrence of a conglomerate and sometimes of a breccia at the base of the phosphatic chalk;
accidental repetition of conglomeratic zones; coarse-grained
and fragmentary character of the components of the basal
phosphatic chalks; (12) immediately convey the picture of a
highly agitated environment of deposition which seems to
imply the vicinity of an emerged land.

The petrographic study of the underlying and overlying chalks combined with that of the components of the phosphatic formation itself, without providing a complete solution to the problem of the generating environment of our phosphatic chalks, nevertheless contributes several fundamental data pertaining to it.

The chalks with *M.c. anguinum* and with *B. quadrata* between which the phosphorites are intercalated, appear characterized petrographically, by the occurrence of a few *Foraminifers*, intact or fragmented, with a very thin test and enclosed within an extremely fine-grained and largely predominant matrix which never displays a single particle that could be identified as detrital quartz.

The conglomeratic base of the phosphatic deposit consists essentially of pebbles of chalk phosphatized to a variable degree, in general highly perforated, and incrusted or not by organisms. These pebbles have all been derived from the underlying chalk with *M.c. anguinum* and are associated with reworked fragments of phosphatic chalk. The basal conglomerate never shows a single pebble, however small, foreign to the chalky environment.

Most of the phosphatic grains consist of thick-shelled Foraminifers, very well preserved, filled with and surrounded by calcium phosphate, and associated with numerous debris of bony tissue. In spite of the coarse-grained character of the chalk, detrital minerals including quartz are always missing from the thin sections.

The transformations of the underlying chalk, (13) the occurrence of the basal conglomeratic chalk and the changes undergone by the foraminiferal fauna—to mention only the major features—lead to the conclusion that an important disturbance preceded the deposition of the phosphatic chalk.

If one wishes to narrow down the question, it is sufficient to examine the insoluble residues of all the deposits involved and to observe that neither the amount, nor the composition of the insoluble residue of the phosphatic chalk has been modified to any appreciable extent. For instance, the very minute and rather rare quartz granules, released by the solution of a fragment of chalk with *M.c. anguinum* and with *B. quadrata*, occur with the same characteristics in the phosphatic chalk.

Obviously, *it looks as if the important disturbance which initiated the formation of the phosphatic chalks of the Paris Basin, did not modify in any respect the relationships between the phosphatic basin and the neighboring shorelines.* As I wrote in 1897 [4] : "This rupture of equilibrium has particularly affected certain parts of the Basin, uplifting them . . . The phosphatic constituents were generated over such areas, temporarily submitted to depth conditions recalling those of shorelines . . . *The relationships between these particular places and the shoreline have not been changed in any respect, detrital minerals were brought to them in the same proportion as in the past . . .*" (14)

In summary, the phosphatic chalk is a sediment typically *detrital* by its phosphatic constituents, and *pelagic* by its matrix. In other words, it is *a detrital deposit generated in a pelagic environment.*

This concept, illustrated by a single example in 1897, contained the essence of a leading idea the great impact of which was to be demonstrated by my subsequent investigations.

In the present state of our knowledge we are compelled to conclude that such conditions of sedimentation, genetically related to large-scale submarine disturbances, are unknown in present seas.

In order to appreciate the importance of what appeared temporarily as an anomaly, it was necessary to find out whether the observed fact was indeed of exceptional nature, or whether it was susceptible of repetition in the ancient seas. A quick look at the phosphorites of North Africa will provide us with the elements of a general law.

2. *Phosphorites of North Africa.*

The Suessonian phosphorites of Tunisia and Algeria, as well as those of Morocco of Cretaceous and Cenozoic age, are different from those of France in many respects. Actually, there is only one essential difference, and it precisely pertains to our problem.

In most of the cases, the phosphatic formation of the Paris Basin consists of a single bed of phosphatic chalk displaying the characteristics mentioned above. Of course, a few exceptions to this rule [5] do occur, as instructive as the phosphorites of North Africa (15), but the conclusions drawn from their analysis would not have the general significance of those derived from the study of the phosphorites of North Africa. Indeed, in Tunisia, Algeria and Morocco, the phosphatic formation always consists of a series of phosphatic beds; occasionally they may be extremely numerous. Such is the case of most of the Tunisian deposits. It is precisely this repetition, observed over a wide surface, which makes them so interesting to us.

The quarried beds and many others begin under always similar conditions expressed by modifications of the underlying bed. The latter is either eroded or perforated, or simultaneously eroded and perforated; furthermore, quite often fragments have been torn away from it and incorporated in the basal portion of the phosphatic layer which consequently displays a very coarse-grained character. In summary, the phosphatic formation, considered as a whole, has been affected by a series of disturbances which created on the sea floor a change of environmental conditions, favorable to the generation of phosphate grains.

The two following examples, belonging to the Tunisian phosphorites, emphasize the amplitude of the modifications resulting from these disturbances. In central Tunisia, very fine-grained limestones with *Globigerina* are abruptly replaced by phosphates consisting of large grains containing Diatoms to the exclusion of any *Globigerina*. In southern Tunisia, more or less argillaceous sediments are replaced under similar conditions by large accumulations of phosphatic grains containing numerous Diatoms and a few Radiolarians.

As a general rule, such ruptures of equilibrium (16) generate an important change of the sedimentary influxes, and simultaneously give to the new deposits a coarse-grained character, often accentuated by the occurrence of true pebbles; at first glance, the whole picture suggests the idea of typical detrital sediments. Should one therefore conclude, as was done in the past, for the phosphatic chalks of northern France, that these phosphates were generated near a shoreline? No. In every case, the coarse-grained character has been generated in the open sea, without any change of the relationships with the emerged land. The same conclusion applies to the phosphatic formation of southern Tunisia which contains abundant and large calcareous pebbles (*boulets, pars*), because all of them, without a single exception, are derived from the phosphatic complex itself.

After all, one finds here, developed on a large scale and applied to all the phosphates of North Africa, the concept reached as a conclusion of the study of the phosphatic chalks of the Paris Basin: *The ruptures of equilibrium have created in the open sea environmental conditions generating deposits, the physical characters of which make erroneously assume the proximity of a shoreline*. Not only do the traces of this aberrant regime extend over an extensive area, but in many places the ruptures of equilibrium have been repeated many times, and on each occasion they have led to the same suite of transformations of the sedimentary materials. (17)

3. *Conclusions*

The very brief study just completed has shown the occurrence of processes which, at particular times, were extremely common in ancient seas, and of which no expression is to be found in present seas.

II. DEPOSITS OF OOLITIC IRON ORES

The history of oolitic iron ores is, in many respects, a blueprint of that of sedimentary phosphorites. Both occur as coarse-grained sediments, always in sharp contrast with the enclosing deposits and widely distributed in time and space.

As the phosphorites, the oolitic iron ores of a given deposit are concentrated in one or several beds. Whenever, under the most favorable conditions, a repetition of beds occurs, a basin as that of Longwy-Briey is generated which displays up to six distinct layers.

All the features pertaining to the mode of occurrence or the composition of the oolitic iron ores indicate rapid or sudden changes of the physical conditions of the environment, that is ruptures of equilibrium. It seems to me unquestionable that the rule proposed in 1897 for the sedimentary phosphorites of the Paris Basin, applies unrestrictedly to the oolitic iron ores (18). I said as follows: "*An intimate relationship exists between the occurrence of phosphorite deposits in the Paris Basin and the ruptures of equilibrium of the seas.*" [6] If "phosphorite" in the above statement were replaced by "oolitic iron ore", the formula would still perfectly apply to our knowledge of the conditions of generation of such ores.

In summary, "*the sedimentation which generated the oolitic iron ores characterizes basins undergoing uplifting, deeply disturbed by ruptures of equilibrium and submitted to the influence of currents acting as agents of submarine transportation and erosion.*" [7]

The environmental analogy is further supported by observations which recall, down to the smallest detail, those which, in the case of the phosphatic chalks, led me to the conclusion reached in 1897 (p. 13). While investigating the Liassic iron ores of the Southern Jura and of the Mont d'Or, near Lyon, I have observed a very striking opposition between two sets of facts. On the one hand, numerous traces of very powerful mechanical actions such as: generation of pebbles of ore at the expense of the formation in the process of being deposited; channelling erosion; fragmentation of numerous Ammonites and Belemnites; comminution of crinoidal debris to a degree as yet never observed; abrasion and decortication of large oolites, etc.; on the other hand almost complete absence of detrital grains of quartz; very small size of such grains whenever they accidentally occur;

decrease of the size and thickness (19) of the tests of Foraminifers, etc. In general, the facts are such that in spite of all the stratigraphical data suggesting the proximity of shorelines, one is compelled to admit that *the ores have, so to speak, not received any contribution from the emerged land, and that the reworked materials have been derived from the oolitic ore itself and from deposits located in the open sea.*

In short, these ores are like the phosphatic chalks of the Paris Basin and the phosphorites of North Africa insofar as *"their formation is closely related to local or regional ruptures of equilibrium, which do not necessarily affect the shorelines themselves, but generate, at a variable distance from them, littoral or sublittoral conditions, extremely favorable to the formation of oolitic iron ores."* [8]

Actually, the history of the oolitic iron ores is more complicated than that of the phosphorites, because it implies a mineralogical evolution consisting of numerous stages and affecting to a variable degree the cement itself. Such an evolution is expressed by a cycle of changes, in which originally calcareous components, such as oolites and organisms, are transformed into iron carbonate, then into iron silicate and eventually into iron oxide. These mineralogical changes, sometimes even more numerous, take place under such conditions that *when the deposition of a bed of oolitic iron ore ends, its history, no matter how complicated, is virtually completed."* [9] Its mineralogical evolution in particular is finished, except in the case where such a bed located near the surface (20), undergoes late modifications due to meteoric agents. However these processes are negligible in comparison with the changes which took place before and after the deposition of the oolites. The fundamental feature to remember is that *the history of ferruginous oolites takes place under the sea.*

[This final statement still holds true today, although recent investigations on the origin of sedimentary iron ores have not confirmed Cayeux's assumption that ferruginous oolites began as calcareous oolites and underwent successive changes into iron carbonate, iron silicate and eventually iron oxide. It is presently considered that the carbonate, silicate and oxide phases were generated as primary deposits in relation to different environmental conditions. (See for instance: H.L. James, Sedimentary facies of iron formations: *Econ. Geology*, 1954, vol. 49, pp. 235-293; H. Borchert, Genesis of marine sedimentary iron ores: *Bull. Inst. Mining Metall.*, 1960, No. 640, (*Trans.*: vol. 69, No. 9), pp. 261-279; L. Bubenicek, Géologie des minerais de fer oolithiques: *Mineralium Deposita*, 1968, vol. 3, pp. 89-108.]

III. CONCLUSIONS

In the light of the data summarized in the preceding pages, the generation of sedimentary phosphorites and of oolitic iron ores reveals the intervention of a series of processes which are nowhere active at present. Their numerous manifestations, in time and space, compel us to consider their activity in a realistic fashion, in other words, as an extremely important factor in the formation of ancient sediments.

In the present state of knowledge, the following processes should be considered as ancient:

1. The fundamental role played by the ruptures of equilibrium of the seas in the generation of phosphorites and oolitic iron ores.

2. The creation, under the influence of such disturbances, of submarine areas, where, away from shorelines, sediments are generated with a littoral or sublittoral facies, which may be misinterpreted in the field.

3. The very rapid submarine evolution of ferruginous compounds over unstable sea bottoms (21), a process with no single example known in present seas.

The investigation of these two kinds of deposits considered under new viewpoints shall bring additional data in favor of our opinion. (22)

CHAPTER II

ROLE OF CALCIUM PHOSPHATE IN THE PRESERVATION OF MICROORGANISMS AND CONSEQUENCES

From a brief study of the phosphatic chalks of the Paris Basin, I have concluded in 1897 that the replacement, even incomplete, of an ancient foraminiferal mud by calcium phosphate leads to the preservation of numerous shells otherwise destroyed outside the replaced areas. [10] Based upon additional knowledge, one can add that this state of preservation is not unique to the ancient phosphatized muds with Foraminifers. The phosphatic nodules of the Culm of the Pyrenees, containing very delicate Radiolarians, and those of the phosphates of North Africa, replete with remains of microplankton, particularly Diatoms, show a perfect preservation of microorganisms. Exceptions to this rule occur, but they shall not be discussed here. In short, these observations acquire today a more general significance, and one can state that throughout the ancient sedimentary record, calcium phosphate (23) plays, with respect to calcareous or siliceous microorganisms, the role of a highly preserving agent.

The calcium phosphate of the concretions dredged by the "Challenger" from the *Globigerina* ooze of the Indian Ocean is an exception to the above-stated rule. The analysis of these concretions by J. Murray and A.F. Renard shows how they have been gradually invaded by calcium phosphate until a final stage of concretionary phosphate was reached in which all traces of Foraminifers have disappeared. [11]

Therefore, *calcium phosphate which in ancient seas has perfectly preserved microorganisms, is capable of destroying them in present seas.* Consequently, *in this particular domain, the present deposits are those which display the most far-reaching changes.*

The study of the phosphatic concretions of the *Globigerina* oozes of the Indian Ocean brings a new and valuable argument supporting the idea repeatedly stated in my previous works, that the *submarine environment plays a fundamental role in the transformations undergone by sediments after their deposition.* Furthermore, it shows, once more, that *present processes are far from being the truthful image of past ones.*(24)

CHAPTER III

PROCESSES OF SUBMARINE REWORKING

My attention has been drawn on the existence and frequency of these particular processes for the first time during a study of the Mesozoic oolitic iron ores of France. Subsequently, I was able to observe them in equally favorable conditions during a general investigation of sedimentary phosphorites. Without exaggeration it may be said that, in the present state of knowledge, examples of the action of these processes are very numerous.

Although the ferruginous and phosphatic environments do not by themselves provide all the data for a demonstration of that subject, I shall still derive from them all the examples to be discussed below.

I. FERRUGINOUS ENVIRONMENT

In the Hettangian and until the Barremian, the oolitic iron ores of France display reworked ferruginous materials, *always derived from the bed of which they are an integrant part.* Regardless of their origin, these materials imply (25) that the ore in the process of formation was continuously undergoing reworking somewhere, while being deposited. Conditions are such that only the ferruginous bed being deposited is the source for the materials. The underlying layer remains completely foreign to the process of reworking. Even in the case of a series of superposed ore beds as in Lorraine, not a single reworked component originates from pre-existing layers.

In order for such a situation to arise, the basin of sedimentation must undergo uplifting at one or several places. Furthermore, the uplifting should be regulated in such a way that during the entire span of time corresponding to the deposition of a particular bed, the reworking would provide only fragments of ore without any contribution whatsoever from the substratum. In short, the rupture of equilibrium must generate shoals, perhaps very close to the surface of the water, and continuously eroded by currents.

This process, far from being unique, is repeated with a great frequency in all the investigated ores, so that it becomes of general occurrence.

The history of the fragments of reworked ores, which is by no means simple, may occasionally become complicated by double reworking. A fragment broken loose from a layer being formed, then re-incorporated into it, may be pulled out a second time together with a portion of the surrounding rock and again included in the parent-rock. Such examples are not rare at all and among the best expressions of the great instability of the sea floor.

The study of the reworking processes of fragments (26) of oolitic iron ore, under the above-mentioned conditions, is directly related to the problem of the mineralogical evolution of the materials. Indeed, such a study demonstrates that the evolution of the oolitic iron ores is extremely rapid and encompasses precisely the period of accumulation of the constituents of a particular bed. Therefore, this entire evolution is a submarine process.

II. PHOSPHATIC ENVIRONMENT

Reworking processes are known in the phosphatic environment both in the granular and nodular phosphorites.
1. Exceptionally, they occur on a large scale, at the beginning of the formation of the ore beds, immediately after the rupture of equilibrium which generated the environment favorable to the deposition of the phosphates. In this case, as soon as a bed was being deposited, it already contributed materials to the reworking processes. This is exactly what happens in the oolitic iron ores.

Furthermore, one observes within a given bed, rare fragments of phosphate, rounded or irregularly-shaped, which are much larger than the grains and contain a variable and often very high number of constituents. In general, these fragments differ from the surrounding phosphate by the smaller size of their grains and a greater development of their cement, (27) which is usually phosphatized. Truly, it is not always possible to demonstrate that these materials have been derived from the very layer enclosing them. But this is obvious whenever the phosphatic formations are reduced to one single layer, or when the reworked fragments occur within the lowest bed of a phosphatic complex. Examples which unquestionably demonstrate processes of submarine reworking at the expense of a given bed are numerous and striking enough to show the close similarity between the generating environments of phosphorites and oolitic iron ores.

2. The processes of submarine reworking are very frequent in the deposits of nodular phosphorites. They are particularly of common occurrence in the history of the Albian nodules of the Paris Basin. [12] From their study I have reached the conclusion that each concentration implies several reworkings, the last of which represents the final deposition of the nodules within a matrix which is never the parent-rock of the reworked materials. In general, the displacement is toward the open sea, but the opposite situation may be observed for a small proportion of the materials.

Extremely striking examples of submarine reworking are provided by the deposits of Cenomanian nodules of the Paris Basin. [13] Following (28) an absolute rule, the composition of these nodules is entirely different from that of the chalky groundmass cementing them. As in the previous case, the reworking—which may be twofold—implies a displacement either toward the open sea or toward the shoreline.

Other rather frequent examples could be called upon to stress the same concept.

3. Phosphatic concretions occur in present seas where they are preferentially concentrated in green muds and sands. The

study of J. Murray and A.F. Renard of the nodules dredged by the "Challenger" shows that the minerals and organisms they contain are identical to those of the enclosing sediments. Therefore, the authors have concluded that these concretions were generated *in situ*. [14] We already know that the exact opposite opinion is required in the case of the phosphatic nodules of the ancient seas which, with a few exceptions, have been reworked either within the deposit from which they derive, or in a sediment appreciably different from the one enclosing them.

III. CONCLUSIONS

Among oolitic iron ores and sedimentary phosphorites, the occurrence and frequency of submarine reworking, at the expense of beds being deposited, represent, in the present state of knowledge, (29) a process characteristic of ancient seas. Obviously, its expression is conditioned by a certain instability of the sea bottom, capable of disturbing sedimentation and of leading to the immediate reworking of its products. Actually, this process is another aspect of the ruptures of equilibrium, which instead of appearing as an anomaly in the past, operates as a normal mechanism in the history of many ancient sediments. (30)

CHAPTER IV

TRANSPORTATION OF MATERIALS OF
PELAGIC ORIGIN INTO THE NERITIC ENVIRONMENT

This process should not be considered accidental or as purely scientific curiosity, but as the expression of conditions which have apparently reached a great amplitude during the formation of the phosphates in Tunisia, and particularly in the basin of Gafsa.

Phosphatic grains, generated in a pelagic environment, replete with frustules of Diatoms occasionally associated with a few very delicate tests of surface-living Radiolarians, and always devoid of detrital minerals, have been transported by currents into areas of the sea floor submitted to a continuous neritic sedimentation and incorporated into a sequence of deposits containing thick concentrations of oysters and intercalations of large pebbles. [15]

Similar facts have been observed in several instances, during the investigation of sedimentary phosphorites, but at no other time and at no other place, by far, have they been expressed on such a large scale. (31)

The numerous phosphatic concretions dredged on the Agulhas Bank, south of the Cape of Good Hope, and certainly formed well before present times, also afford very striking examples.

Their characteristics lead to the inescapable conclusion that nodules, formed at the expense of *Globigerina oozes*, have been removed from their generating environment and transported to adjacent parts of the sea floor where *green sands* were deposited. This conclusion implies another one. It looks as if these nodules, during their reworking, had been transported from a sediment much more pelagic than

16

terrigenous, into a typically terrigenous one, and consequently from certain depths to much shallower ones. [16]

Until further information, it is reasonable to state that
present seas are far from providing the required conditions
for a continuous and long-lasting transportation into the zone
of terrigenous deposits of materials generated in the pelagic
environment. (32)

CHAPTER V

EVAPORATION PROCESSES IN OPEN SEA

At present, I have only one example from the Gothlandian of Normandy which pertains to this subject. [17] The features of this bed encountered by a deep drilling at Danneville (Calvados) have permitted to reach the following synthetical view of the generating environment: an extremely shallow sea supporting an unusually abundant plankton, receiving only a negligible inflow of materials from the coast, and capable of generating evaporation products.

A limestone bed, encountered at a depth of 285.40 m. and related to a lithological complex of pelagic character, appears replete with microscopic crystals of calcite which can immediately be recognized as pseudomorphs after gypsum. Some of them are lenticular, but the great majority display distinct monoclinic shapes and grade to the former through all intermediate forms. [18] These crystals, although smaller, recall very closely those of the lagoonal Cenozoic of the vicinity of Paris. [19] (33) Their interpretation as calcite pseudomorphs after gypsum is unquestionable, and their possible derivation from pyrite cannot be considered.

All the facts tend to demonstrate that the lagoonal episode which generated them is located in the open sea. In order to understand such conditions, one must visualize waters so shallow that a very weak rupture of equilibrium would be sufficient to create locally a lagoonal environment. This concept is in perfect agreement with the interpretation of the graptolite-rich seas reached by authors like A. W. Grabau, M. O' Connell and W.R. King who have studied in detail the ampelitic environment.

It seems almost superfluous to add that present oceans are far from displaying similar conditions. (34)

CHAPTER VI

SUBMARINE CEMENTATION OF SEDIMENTS

The study of the processes of submarine reworking presented briefly in the previous pages furnishes many data regarding this problem. Whether we are dealing with the reworking of oolitic iron ores, of sedimentary phosphorites, or of the limestones and dolomites intercalated between certain phosphatic formations of North Africa, etc., the problem of the physical state of the reworked materials is raised every time.

In many instances, I have observed fragments of reworked ores, displaying along their margins either ferruginous oolites or phosphatic grains, or very resistant organic debris such as crinoidal columnals, truncated by the dynamic action of the waters without any of these constituents having been broken loose from the reworked fragments. Therefore, the state of aggregation of the constituents, cemented either by a ferruginous compound or by amorphous calcium phosphate, was in a very advanced stage of completion at the time of the submarine fragmentation of these particular ores.

One can even state that, in numerous cases, this cementation has been very rapid (35) as demonstrated by the fragments of ores reworked at the very base of the layer from which they originated.

The same conclusion applies to the calcareous and dolomitic materials, similarly reworked under the sea. I shall purposely not recall here the numerous and significant observations, collected during the analysis of all types of sedimentary rocks, and which testify in the same manner.

Obviously, the very rapid submarine cementation of the investigated sediments is one of the consequences of the instability of the sea floor, in other words, of ruptures of equilibrium displayed in particular by the history of the oolitic iron ores and of the phosphorites. The absence of such disturbances in present seas leads *ipso facto* to that of cementation processes almost simultaneous with sedimentation.

This is another instance showing that the conditions of ancient seas are very often different from those of present seas. (36)

[However, recent studies have revealed, for instance, an increasing number of examples of submarine cementation of modern carbonates, although on a relatively restricted scale, from reef and shallow water conditions to intermediate oceanic depths. See for instance: A.G. Fischer and R.E. Garrison, Carbonate lithification on the sea floor: *Jour. Geol.*, 1967, vol. 75, pp. 488-496; I.G. Macintyre, E.W. Mountjoy and B.F.D. D'Anglejan, An occurrence of submarine cementation of carbonate sediments off the west coast of Barbados, W.I.: *Jour. Sed. Petrology*, 1968, vol. 38, pp. 660-664; G. Thompson, V.T. Bowen, W.G. Melson and R. Cifelli, Lithified carbonates from the deep-sea of the equatorial Atlantic: *Jour. Sed. Petrology*, 1968, vol. 38, pp. 1305-1312; O.P. Bricker, R.N. Ginsburg, L.S. Land and F.T. Mackenzie (editors), *Carbonate cements*, Sp. Publ. No. 3, 1969, Bermuda Biological Station, St. George's West, Bermuda, 325 p. also published as O.P. Bricker (editor), *Carbonate Cements*, 1970, The Johns Hopkins University Press; the special issue of *Sedimentology* entitled Lithification of carbonate sediments, 1 and 2: 1969, vol. 12, ½, ¾; L.S. Land and T.F. Goreau, Submarine lithification of Jamaican reefs: *Jour. Sed. Petrology*, 1970, vol. 40, pp. 457-462.]

CHAPTER VII

PROCESSES OF MOLECULAR CONCENTRATION

The arguments that may be derived from such processes are afforded by the siliceous concentrations which lead in particular to the formation of cherts, and the calcareous segregations which generate bodies called nodules, kidney-shaped stones or concretions.

I. FORMATION OF CHERTS

It is well known that cherts occur within chalks in the form of numerous nodules, interstratified layers—unquestionably more widespread than the nodules (*rognons*)—and occasionally as veins oblique to bedding. [The French word used here is *"silex"*, a term restricted to the siliceous inclusions of the chalk which are usually dark-colored to black. These black cherts are sometimes referred to as "flint".] Furthermore, cherts are generally considered to result from the segregation of silica, originally scattered throughout the sediments as organic remains, mainly Sponge spicules. Most geologists have assumed that the concentration of this organic silica occurred relatively late, either during the period of emergence of the chalky sediments, or mostly after their complete emergence. If necessary, supporters of this concept do not fail to quote an argument erroneously considered (37) irrefutable, namely that submarine dredgings have everywhere confirmed the lack of siliceous concretions in the process of being formed on the sea floor. Consequently, present processes remain foreign to the generation of cherts.

The investigation of the chalky cliffs of the Channel, which display ideal conditions of observation, as well as the study of the phosphates of Tunisia, provide data which point toward an entirely different solution of this problem.

1. *Cherts of the chalk of the Paris Basin*

A. In the region of Saint-Valéry-en Caux (Seine-Inférieure), one can observe in the chalk with *M.c. anguinum* "a very regular and tabular bed of black chert, 2 to 3 centimeters thick, abruptly interrupted and replaced by a chert breccia, [20] generated at its expense and extending over a hundred meters. Then, the tabular bed reappears just as abruptly as it had disappeared, to be replaced again further on by another breccia. Fragments may either occur next to each other and concentrated over a thickness of 8 to 10 centimeters, or in rare instances widely scattered within slightly coarser-grained white chalk, and throughout a thickness which may reach 30 centimeters. A study of the breccia itself reveals, in addition to randomly oriented large fragments (38), splinters, shards and granules, sometimes visible only with a hand lens because of the high degree of fragmentation". [21] Unquestionably, the same bed has been the parent-rock throughout the outcrop. It is furthermore possible to demonstrate that the number and the size of the fragments scattered in the breccia are such that if they were put back into reciprocal contact, they would represent the normal continuation of the interrupted bed. It should be pointed out that the chalks underlying and overlying the breccia are identical by their physical characteristics and intimate composition with those of the chert bed.

B. The same process of fragmentation has occurred, on a large scale, at the expense of nodular cherts. There are numerous examples of nodules changed into chert breccias, not only along the cliffs of the Channel, but also inland.

Breccias generated at the expense of the cherts of a Turonian chalk, all provided with a thick patina, occur between the Cap d'Antifer and Etretat. At each place, the debris entirely unsorted, invariably display all the features of the non-fragmented cherts—patina included—of that particular bed. If the cherts *in situ* happen accidentally to be pink, the breccia formed at their expense consists of fragments which are also pink in color.

In general, the change of chert into breccia has occurred either at the expense of an isolated nodule, or of a series of nodules aligned in a same plane (39), and without the introduction of a single constituent foreign to the chalky environment. In both cases, it is impossible to assume late processes to explain the fragmentation and displacement of the debris, because the bed overlying the broken cherts does not show any effect of such an action.

As mysterious as this process of *in situ* fragmentation of the cherts might appear, we cannot escape the conclusion reached in 1929, namely that "nodular and tabular cherts are formed under such conditions that they can be reworked within the bed of chalk in which they were generated". [22] Actually, their formation follows so closely the deposition of the chalky mud on the sea floor that it may be rightly considered contemporaneous with sedimentation.

In that respect, present seas are far from being similar to past ones.

2. *Cherts of the phosphorites of Tunisia*

The phosphorites of Tunisia, and particularly those of eastern Tunisia, provide very striking examples of the submarine reworking of cherts in which evidence of a very rapid concentration of silica during sedimentation can be observed.

Dolomites with cherts, enclosed between the *banc gris* and the *banc constant* of the mine of M'Zaïta (Constantine), contain a discontinuous intercalation of a calcareous and siliceous conglomerate, .10 to .15 m thick, characterized by pebbles of a well-defined type of chert, derived (40) from *in situ* cherts, occurring .15 to .20 m underneath the conglomerate. Elsewhere, and in the same bed, a similar reworking may be observed in which the distance between the source-rock and the chert pebbles has been reduced to .10 m. In both instances, all the reworked constituents of the conglomerate are derived from the phosphatic formation without any intervention from the emerged land.

The deposit of Rebiba, in central Tunisia, allows observations of the same kind and no less instructive. A limestone with cherts, often destroyed by erosional effects, occurs between the two major beds of the phosphatic complex. [23]

A. Nodules, set free by erosional actions, are strewn over the surface of the limestone, proving that they were already formed when the limestone was undergoing submarine erosion.

B. Cherts which erosional processes have uncovered at the upper part of the limestone and to which they are still attached by their base, display numerous small perforations. This feature demonstrates that the nodules pre-existed the deposition of the overlying bed, and consequently were formed on the sea floor.

3. *Conclusions*

The preceding data, which could be easily multiplied if necessary, clearly show that the floor of the ancient seas generated numerous cherts whereas (41) the present submarine environmental conditions apparently seem unsuitable to the concentration of organic silica. Therefore, at the time of formation of the chalk and of other variably calcareous sediments, submarine processes, not active at present, [24] played a fundamental role in the history of silica.

II. FORMATION OF CALCAREOUS NODULES

Very striking examples of this kind are provided by the oolitic iron ores of Lorraine and by the phosphorites of southern Tunisia.

1. *Nodules of the oolitic iron ores of Lorraine*

A systematic investigation of the iron ores of Lorraine has shown that whenever calcium carbonate ceases to be an

Library
I.U.P.
Indiana, Pa.

552.5   C 317p

accessory constituent, it strongly tends to occur as concentrations of all sizes, of infinitely variable shapes, but generally limited by curved surfaces. Regardless of their size and shape, these concentrations are called kidney-shaped stones (*rognons*) or *nodules*. Among other types, one observes spheroidal and lenticular bodies, free or welded together, generating in such (42) instances mammillated or irregularly-shaped masses of all sizes which may grade into poorly-developed frameworks enclosing the normal ore. All these calcareous concentrations have a very marked tendency to be elongated parallel to bedding. The nodules are associated or not with true thin beds, lenticular on a large scale and relaying each other along strike.

In order to obtain a correct idea of the importance of these kinds of segregations and of the appearance they can give to the ferruginous formations, it should be recalled that they may build more than 50% of certain ores. Their dimensions are also very variable; for instance, a given lenticular concentration measures 10 to 20 centimeters along its longest axis, while another reaches 1.5 m. [25]

From our particular standpoint, these nodules are extremely interesting because of the possibility of assigning them a very precise age limit. For instance, some calcareous nodules of the gray bed of Valleroy (Meurthe-et-Moselle) have their upper part truncated and abraded by beds of ferruginous limestones. [26] This situation does not at all represent an interruption in the development of the nodules, which could take place in any direction, but a true destruction following their final growth, due to the erosional action of bottom currents. Consequently, *the generation of the nodules is, so to speak, contemporaneous with the deposition of the ore bed enclosing them*. It is important to stress that on the basis of our knowledge of the degree of frequency of the nodules, this conclusion applies to neoformations which (43) by themselves constitute a very appreciable proportion of the ferruginous complex of the Basin of Briey.

2. *Calcareous nodules of the phosphorites of southern Tunisia*

The phosphatic formation of southern Tunisia also contains calcareous nodules which, although not as widespread as those of the ores of Lorraine, nevertheless provide data of great significance. These nodules called *boulets* [27] by the mining operators, are concentrated and aligned in rows, either in the phosphate itself, or within the marls alternating with the ore beds. Of greatly variable size and generally rounded shape, they have two distinct origins. Those of interest for our demonstration are large elongated blocks, reaching 1 meter or more in size and belonging to the group of the *miches* (round loaves of bread). This variety of *boulets*, for instance, is related to the argillaceous-phosphatic intercalation of the upper bed mined at Metlaoui (Oued Lousif).

The generation of these constituents is generally explained by a segregation of the calcium carbonate, in a marly environment, a process which gives them the character of concretions. It is rarely possible to date the formation of these concentrations which play, with respect to the marls, the role of the siliceous accidents in chalks and limestones. In the present case (44), the problem has a very clear solution since some of these *miches* are characterized by perforations of organic origin, exclusively developed in their upper part. Therefore, their differentiation is the result of a submarine process and did not occur after emergence. In other words, the generation of such concentrations is essentially contemporaneous with sedimentation. This is precisely the same conclusion reached through the study of the nodules of the oolitic iron ores of Lorraine, eroded on the sea floor.

III. CONCLUSIONS

Regardless of the nature of the concentrated materials and their generation in calcareous, marly or phosphatic environments, the inescapable conclusion is always the same. In general, and with the exception of a few rare cases among siliceous segregations, the processes of molecular concentration of silica and calcium carbonate belong to submarine phenomena.

As of today, one is allowed to conclude that in the absence of similar concentrations on the floor of the present oceans, a broad chapter of the history of sedimentary rocks is deprived of any additional data resulting from the knowledge of present processes. (45)

CHAPTER VIII

NODULAR STRUCTURE OF THE CHALK [28]

It would be a mistake to believe that ruptures of equilibrium are restricted only to sedimentary environments which generate phosphorites and oolitic iron ores. Indeed, since long ago, it has been demonstrated that they have deeply affected sediments, such as the typical chalk commonly considered as a quiet water deposit *par excellence*.

The nodular chalks reported by Ed. Hébert in the Paris Basin, [29] then by W. Whitaker [30], Ch. Barrois [31], and others in England, are nothing but the products of disturbances acting, in most of the cases, (46) on the sea floor within a pelagic environment.

Contributions to the study of the nodular chalk by the above-mentioned authors, and by others as well, suggest that the change of the normal chalk into a nodular one is always the consequence of a movement of the sea floor, leading or not to an emergence capable of attaining a large amplitude. The consequences are environmental changes, such as an interruption of sedimentation, lithologic modifications of the chalk and appreciable faunal changes if the rupture of equilibrium becomes a general disturbance.

The beds of nodular chalk to be discussed here belong to two types, neither of which implies any reworking whatsoever of the materials. The most numerous of them by far, which display only an aberrant texture, are interstratified within the chalk and may be traced along strike for hundreds and hundreds of meters. The others, which result from an unusually accentuated disturbance, rest with a very clear unconformity on the underlying chalk.

The region of Etretat (Seine-Inférieure) displays, in particular, examples of large-scale unconformity and of numerous nodular beds within the *M.c. anguinum* chalk. One can see beds of nodular chalk arranged in small concentric depressions truncated on top by a horizontal nodular chalk.[32] (47) Numerous nodular beds, whenever traced laterally, become closer to each other and rapidly merge into a single one, etc. In that particular region, *the beds of nodular chalk may increase in number to the extent that they locally occupy more space than the interbedded white chalk*. Such a situation shows the importance and the frequency of the disturbances which affected the sedimentation of the chalk in that part of the Paris Basin. As a matter of fact, it is within the realm of the chalks most affected by these ruptures of equilibrium, that the fragmentation of the cherts on the sea floor reaches its greatest development (p. 38).

These nodular chalks occur as perfectly individualized beds with an average thickness reduced to a few decimeters. They grade into the underlying chalk, but are limited upwards by a generally irregular surface which clearly separates them from the overlying chalk. Furthermore, it is not unusual for that surface to display numerous perforations of pholads.

Actually, these chalks have only an apparent nodular aspect, and one would look in vain for a real nodule. As a general rule, these chalks, whenever perfectly preserved, consist of non-cemented chalky residues set within an extremely hard stony framework. But, when they occur at the foot of sea cliffs, undergoing the continuous erosion of the waves, they gradually lose their soft portions and eventually turn into a calcareous framework which obviously resulted from a very irregular mass cementation. In cross-section, the framework seems to consist (48) of independent nuclei of cemented chalk whereas they become welded to each other inside.

In addition to this transformation, one can observe in places, the local disappearance through the effects of submarine erosion, of the bed of chalk directly overlying a nodular layer.

It is most certain, as recognized by Ed. Hébert in the Paris Basin and by Ch. Barrois for the chalk of England, that some nodular beds result from very widespread disturbances, while others, much more numerous, imply only local ones. In both cases, the lithologic characters of the modified chalks are similar.

The detailed investigation of these chalks reveals five fundamental facts:

1. The said nodular structure is not at all the consequence of a differential crystallization restricted to certain portions of the chalky mud, because the nodular chalks have exactly the same microstructure as the normal chalks among which they are interbedded.

2. The mineralogical composition is always modified to a certain extent by the addition of three constituents: *glauconite*, *calcium phosphate* and *hematite* which occur in most cases separately, but are occasionally associated. These three substances have not been incorporated to the nodular chalks during their deposition, but added secondarily through replacement taking place at the same time as the disturbances. (49)

3. The organic composition of the chalks, separated by a rupture of equilibrium, may be modified with respect to the frequency or the types of constituents. For instance, the transition between the nodular chalk and the overlying white chalk is accompanied by an abrupt change in the microfauna.

4. Any disturbance, regardless of its importance, does not seem to have appreciably affected the supply of detrital minerals. For instance, in the Senonian nodular chalks, the quartz grains are not more abundant than in the enclosing white chalks.

5. Whether the disturbances are of local nature or display the features of generalized movements, the grading of the nodular chalk into the overlying normal one never implies the occurrence of reworked materials. Once more, it looks as if the disturbances were restricted to the marine environment.

The ruptures of equilibrium, whose effects have just been analyzed, are completely unrelated with those of the Upper Turonian and basal Campanian, which are known to be due to processes of regression and transgression. They result from particular movements of the sea floor, responsible for a temporary interruption of the sedimentation and for the action of currents which erode or not the surface of the chalky mud, but without involving the entire area of the Paris Basin. The mineralization and cementation of the chalk (50) occur at that time as a result of the physico-chemical changes of the environment induced by the uplifting of the sea floor. An increase of depth follows this phase and corresponds to the deposition of the normal white chalk which overlies the nodular chalks. The succession of such events expresses quite well the concept of oscillatory movements proposed by Ch. Barrois, but does not at all correspond to the large-scale processes of emergence postulated by Ed. Hébert.

On the basis of extensive observations, it seems rather obvious that the disturbances recorded by the beds of indurated chalk have not modified the relationship between open sea and shorelines. Even if emergences did occur—an unjustifiable assumption—they would take place in the open sea, outside the limits of coastal influence.

If the disturbances which generated the nodular chalks are to be interpreted according to the above-mentioned deductions, a great environmental instability must be assumed. Nowhere, did this instability express itself with so much intensity and frequency as in the chalk with *M.c. anguinum* of the region of Etretat (Seine-Inférieure). (51)

CONCLUSIONS

The investigation of the nodular chalks and of the disturbances which generated them shows that the ruptures of equilibrium, far from being limited to a complete change in the nature of the sedimentary supplies, and to favoring the development of phosphorites and oolitic iron ores, are actually capable of completely modifying the physical characteristics of the deposits on the sea floor.

The present study leads to a second conclusion, no longer unknown to us, namely that the numerous disturbances which have occurred in the open sea disclose no participation whatsoever of the emerged land. (52)

CHAPTER IX

NODULAR CHALKS AND HARD GROUNDS
OF THE PRESENT OCEANS

The previous study of the nodular chalks, quite naturally raises the problem of the origin of the hard grounds discovered by the "Challenger".

What exactly are the hard grounds? This subject, in spite of its great significance, has not been the topic of a particular analysis by J. Murray and A.F. Renard in the valuable volume entitled "Deep-Sea Deposits" of the collected results of the "Challenger" expedition. The few data pertaining to this question are scattered throughout the "Synoptical tables of the results obtained through the megascopic and microscopic examination of the sediments" (column of "additional observations"). The scanning of these tables is extremely instructive.

I wish to recall that the particular areas, called hard grounds, not overlain by deposits in the process of formation, occur in the realm of the terrigenous and pelagic sediments, and range between 155 and 2,011 meters depth. Such a spread between the depth limits immediately points toward variations in the conditions of formation.

The study of the hard grounds reveals two distinct types: 1. hard grounds of homogeneous composition (53), such as the cemented limestones discovered by the "Blake" along the path of warm currents. Its cruises have revealed that offshore Florida, on the Pourtalès plateau, a cemented limestone is being presently formed between 160 and 500-600 meters depth. This limestone consists of an accumulation of Corals, Echinoderms and Foraminifers; it reaches 97% calcium carbonate. 2. hard grounds of heterogeneous nature, apparently with nodular structure. They are the only ones, at first glance, capable of being the equivalent of our nodular chalks, if a comparison between the two types of deposits is at all warranted.

All considered the question of the hard grounds should be viewed here under two very different viewpoints:

1. To what extent are the investigated nodular chalks related to the materials forming the hard grounds?
2. Regardless of the final conclusion, is the formation of the hard grounds related to past or present geological processes?

1. Among the hard grounds reported by the "Challenger", I shall only mention those which display a *nodular structure*. Their features are as follows:

A.—At a depth of 2,195 meters, between Bermudas and Halifax (Atlantic), on a bottom of blue muds containing 24.61% calcium carbonate (Station 44), several rounded pebbles were found, measuring from 2 to 6 centimeters in diameter, also a few irregular fragments of hardened deposit forming a *conglomerate* of a yellow-green color. Amongst these were "*several (54) rounded, compact, chalky nodules, apparently formed within the deposit*, and measuring from 1 to 3 centimeters in diameter." [33]

B.—In the sea of Banda (Malaysia), between the islands of Banda and Arrou, at a depth of 230 meters (St. 192 A) were collected "many rounded, more or less hardened nodules, composed entirely of the shells of *Globigerina, Pulvinulina* and *Orbulina*", displaying the hardness of calcite. It is "a *Globigerina* ooze, more or less hardened". [34]

C.—In the same region, between Amboine and Samboangan (St. 196), on a hard ground, at a depth of 1,508 meters, the "Challenger" collected fragments of a *conglomerate*, hard, of yellowish-white color, containing 93.7% calcium carbonate. The largest fragments measured 20 by 30 centimeters in size. Thin sections show that most of the material consist of *Foraminifers* and *calcareous Algae*, transformed into a crystalline limestone. Microscopic crystals of calcium carbonate have been formed in all the hollows of the concretions, and the cement is also crystalline. [35]

These nodules are perforated in all directions.

In summary, the first observation indicates a complex deposit of somewhat aberrant composition, containing at the same time pebbles, fragments of a conglomerate, and several nodules perhaps generated *in situ*. The second deposit is the product of reworking of a *Globigerina* sediment, although located at a depth incompatible with the occurrence of a *Globigerina* ooze. [36] The conglomeratic nature (55) and crystalline state of the third deposit rule out any comparison between the investigated chalks and the hard grounds just discussed. In short, despite the impossibility of reaching a well-established opinion without investigating in detail the materials themselves, it seems obvious to me that *the sediments with multiple facies, dredged at the three above-mentioned stations, have nothing at all in common with the composition of the nodular chalks of the Paris Basin.*

2. I am now inclined to believe that to the previously presented hypothesis explaining the hard grounds, another one should be added. It should conform—more than the others do—with our present knowledge of the role played by ruptures of equilibrium in the ancient sedimentation.

In the memoir which I wrote early in my career, on the petrography of the chalk of the Paris Basin, the beds of indurated chalk reported by Ed. Hébert appeared to me as comparable to the hard grounds, a similarity not based on any argument pertaining to their structure. [37]

Later on, and better informed, I was led to ask myself if the generation of hard grounds is not the expression of a general process which is revealed to us only accidentally. Instead of assuming that the currents cement certain areas of the sea floor, could we not suppose that they simply have an erosional action which locally uncovers consolidated sediments, elsewhere covered by the blanket of the muds and oozes (56) presently being deposited? In other words, what has been considered as an exception would be the general rule. The processes of cementation, or at least their effects, revealed in such a manner, would be the consequence of a general metamorphism involving the sediments soon after their deposition. [An interesting anticipation because recent studies have revealed numerous instances of rapid cementation of carbonates after deposition in the Recent as well as throughout the geological record. See for instance, O. P. Bricker *et al.* (editors), *Carbonate cements*, 1969, Bermuda Biological Station for Research, Spec. Publ. No. 3.] This explanation is obviously very hypothetical. Therefore, I would not be surprised if a detailed investigation of the question—based on actual samples—would demonstrate its irrevelance. [38]

Possibly, the origin of the hard grounds of nodular type, could be ancient, even very ancient, and related to a long period of interruption of sedimentation. The study of the phosphates of the Agulhas Bank having shown that phosphatic nodules, almost certainly of Cenozoic age, lie on the sea floor without being buried, [39] one is compelled to assume that sedimentation may be interrupted in certain areas, for long rows of centuries, or, in other words, that the sediments deposited over them are continuously washed away by the currents and therefore cannot be deposited in these particular places. Hence, a double consequence:

1. Occurrence of future gaps in the sedimentary record, independent of any process of emergence;
2. Modification and cementation of particular areas of the sea floor (57) during the period of interruption of the sedimentation, and most probably under the influence of currents. The study of the phosphates of the Culm of the Pyrenees and of the Montagne-Noire has revealed such an interruption of deposition, over an extensive area and during a considerable length of time. [40]

One important fact, resulting from the explorations of the "Blake", should be given serious consideration when attempting to interpret the hard grounds. It is the dredging of phosphatic concretions in the North Atlantic on a hard ground, related to green muds and sands, [41] at a depth of about 600 meters and at $31°57'$ latitude N. This association of hard ground and phosphatic nodules immediately suggests the idea of a comparison with the conditions of occurrence of the phosphorites, whose formation begins by a large-scale disturbance, leading to the cementation and perforation of the substratum of the phosphatic sediments.

CONCLUSIONS

1. Assuming that the hard grounds were comparable in all respects to the nodular chalks of the Paris Basin, this would not demonstrate, *ipso facto*, that present seas are capable of generating nodular structures under the same conditions as the Upper Cretaceous seas, (58), that is under the influence of ruptures of equilibrium.

Actually, the depths presently covered by *Globigerina* ooze, although investigated in numerous instances, have not, as yet, afforded any hint of modifications comparable to the nodular structure of the chalk.

Therefore, one can at least presume that the conditions favorable to the generation of that structure do not occur today, and consequently, that sedimentation proceeds unhindered by the disturbances so frequent in the chalk-generating seas.

2. Without pretending to reach a general conclusion based on a single fact, it is reasonable to ask if the observation collected by the "Blake" does not point the way toward the explanation of the question of the hard grounds. If the answer were positive, *the hard grounds would be the product of ruptures of equilibrium older than the present epoch*.

At any rate, the striking fact to stress is that present processes do not seem to be involved. (59)

CHAPTER X

DOLOMITIZATION OF THE CHALK OF
THE PARIS BASIN

Processes of dolomitization known in present seas are closely related to the development of coral reefs. Very often a similar situation has also been true in the geological past. [Present and past occurrences of dolomitization seem to occur mainly in supratidal and lagoonal environments and to a lesser degree in direct relationship with reef constructions possibly through a process called seepage refluxion. See L.C. Pray and R.C. Murray (editors), *Dolomitization and limestone diagenesis, a symposium*: 1965, S.E.P.M. Spec. Publ. No. 13; R.C. Murray, Hydrology of South Bonaire, N. A.—A rock selective dolomitization model: *Jour. Sed. Petrology*, 1969, vol. 39, pp. 1007-1013.] However, important examples of widespread dolomitization, as displayed in the Carboniferous of France and Belgium and elsewhere, do not show this relationship. This is also true for the accidental dolomitization of the chalk to be discussed here.

1. The generation of certain occurrences of magnesian chalk of the Paris Basin coincides in time with the two greatest disturbances which affected it during the deposition of the chalk.

At two different times during the Upper Cretaceous, the Paris Basin has been the site of events which have deeply affected the chemical and physical nature of the sediments.

The physical and chemical nature of the deposits at the end of the Turonian were influenced by a rupture of equilibrium which included all northern France and England. A tendency toward emergence occurred which generated true chalk conglomerates. (60) The formation of yellow chalks with callosities (*craies jaunes à durillons*)—of low magnesium content—and of calcium phosphates (at Cambrésis and the neighborhood of Lille [42]), is related to this disturbance.

A second and more important rupture of equilibrium is represented by the great Campanian transgression and by an appreciable diminution of the depth of the sea. The chalk has recorded this event in different ways: interruption of sedimentation, erosion, cementation and perforation of the sea floor. It looks as if the transformation of the white chalk with *M.c. anguinum* into a magnesian chalk resulted from an environmental change due to the uplifting of the sea floor which preceded the Campanian transgression. [43]

In addition to widespread disturbances, the Paris Basin also displays examples of very localized movements to which extremely instructive magnesian accidents are related.

The transformation of the white chalk of the vicinity of Etretat into a yellow, hard, crystalline and magnesian chalk is undoubtedly the consequence of an interruption of sedimentation, complicated by erosion and followed by an important change of the nature of the deposits. [44]

The strange deposit of Bimont, in the Oise, related to the chalk with *M.c. anguinum*, also indicates a serious disturbance of the normal sedimentary environment. This is shown by the very clear disconformity between the magnesian chalk and the completely unmodified overlying white chalk. [45] (61) 2. Furthermore, the Paris Basin presents very interesting examples of magnesian accidents of the chalk localized on anticlines and apparently formed at the end of the Cretaceous.

The deposit of Beynes, in Seine-et-Oise, where the modifications of the chalk have been carried to the degree of generating dolomitic sands, occupies the top of an important anticlinal ridge.

The well-known dolomitic sands of the region of Mantes (Eure) are located exactly along the trace of the so-called anticline of the Seine. In a nearby region, numerous dolomitic concentrations (Bueil, Ivry-la-Bataille) are aligned along an anticline.

In the Aisne, where the metamorphosis of the white chalks seems to be a general feature over a widespread area, the zone of dolomitic sands in the vicinity of Montcornet is located along the continuation of the "Axis of the Artois", one of the major dislocations of the Paris Basin. [46]

CONCLUSIONS

This short review of the Cretaceous magnesian accidents of the Paris Basin shows the fundamental fact that *they all derive from the transformation of a chalky mud, and not from a coral reef.*

Moreover, the occurrences of magnesian chalk are closely related to ruptures of equilibrium (62) expressed in two ways: *uplifting of the sea floor*, followed by interruption of sedimentation, submarine processes of cementation and folding, etc. In that respect, it should be recalled that "the geographic distribution of the magnesian accidents coincides with the portion of the Paris Basin where the ruptures of equilibrium reached their maximum frequency and amplitude." [47]

In conclusion, the environmental conditions under which the magnesian accidents of the chalk of the Paris Basin were generated, are entirely different from those occurring in present oceans. In this particular domain, as in the preceding ones, the present is not the continuation of the past. (63)

CHAPTER XI

FOLDING CONTEMPORANEOUS WITH SEDIMENTATION

The question of submarine folding capable of influencing the processes of sedimentation is among those raised by the study of sedimentary phosphorites, cherts, nodular chalks, oolitic iron ores and magnesian chalks.

In that respect, and on the basis of our present knowledge, the most interesting subject by far is that of the calcium phosphates of the Paris Basin. This might be due to the fact that for many years their exploitation has been very carefully observed by J. Gosselet, one of my early teachers.

It is only fair to recall that Henri Lasne [48] was the first one to notice that the phosphatic chalk of the vicinity of Doullens (Somme) was deposited on a sea floor which had just undergone folding, without involving any emergence.

The observations of J. Gosselet [49] have unquestionably demonstrated (64) that *the sea floor which generated the phosphatic chalks, has undergone movements—for a long time unsuspected—which formed folds with very small radius of curvature, the best developed being asymmetrical, isoclinal, overturned and even recumbent.* [50]

These movements are combined with *extremely well-characterized phenomena of transgression and of angular unconformity* [51]

The investigation of the cherts of the chalk in the cliffs of the Channel has revealed similar deformations, also of submarine nature, at a time when the generation of phosphates was not at all involved. In the region of Etretat, I have drawn the attention on the occurrence of cherts distributed as stringers—rarely as continuous beds—, associated or not with beds of nodular chalk, and which form small and very well defined concentric depressions, all being truncated at the top by a horizontal bed of either nodular chalk or chert. [52] There are also stringers of chert forming small concentric depressions, enclosed between two horizontal beds of nodular chalk which truncate them both at the base and at the top. In the same cliffs, one can see cross-bedded stringers of chert, unconformable and transgressive, [53] perfectly expressing the movements which have affected the chalk during its deposition. (65)

The chalk, phosphatic or not, did not only record the submarine formation of embryonic folds. Indeed, there are reasons to believe that the origin of the large-scale ondulations which involve the chalk of the Paris Basin as well as its overlying Eocene and Oligocene sediments, can be traced much farther back in the past than usually assumed. Therefore, in the history of these dislocations, a very long submarine phase should be distinguished, preceding movements which subsequently only accentuated folds that had existed since a long time.

In particular, the study of the submarine magnesian accidents of the chalk of the Paris Basin, considered in the light of their genetic relations with the folds of the chalk (p. 59), demonstrates the intervention of the latter—only as embryonic features—before the fixation of the magnesium in the chalk.

A similar problem, presented by the phosphatic formation of southern Tunisia, implies an analogous solution. Its study clearly demonstrates the pre-existence of large synclines to the deposition of the phosphates and their deep influence on the phosphatic sedimentation.

A like concept may also result from the analysis of the Mesozoic oolitic iron ores of France, [54] and particularly from the study of the oolitic iron ores of Lorraine.

One of the fundamental characteristics of the marine environment which generated our oolitic iron ores (66) is an extremely disturbed type of sedimentation. We have learned previously (p. 24) that from the Hettangian until the

Barremian included, these ores show ferruginous materials, reworked once and even twice, and always derived from the bed of which they are an integrant part. Regardless of their origin, *these fragments demonstrate that the ore in the process of formation was reworked somewhere while being deposited*. From their study, we can deduce, at least in the case of the ores of Lorraine, that *the tendency toward emergence of the portions of the sea floor where the fragmentation of the ores in the process of formation is taking place, has as corollary the generation of shoals, that is of folds on the sea bottom*. Were these ridges dismantled while being formed, or do they most probably represent a real embryonic stage of present-day folds? I have not made any decisive observation in that respect.

CONCLUSIONS

These processes of submarine folding seem to have played an important role, at least in the areas and during the epochs discussed above. They have changed the bathymetrical conditions of the whole or part of the affected basins, leading therefore to modifications of the nature of the sediments and to an increase in the erosive action of currents. An exhaustive study of this question would be out of place here, in spite of its very instructive aspect. (67) From what we have learned until now, I conclude that we are essentially dealing with one modality of ruptures of equilibrium, the great importance of which I have stressed in the preceding pages. The only purpose of their brief discussion in this volume is to emphasize their absence in present seas and hereby to increase the number of processes which seem to belong exclusively to the geological past.(68)

CHAPTER XII

MINERAL SYNTHESES IN SUBMARINE ENVIRONMENT

Before comparing past and present submarine environments with respect to the mineral syntheses which occurred there and still do, it is appropriate to recall the opinion of Sir John Murray and Johan Hjort on mineral neoformations in present oceans. [55]

In essence, these two scientists consider that the depths of the sea are more favorable to the destruction of mineral matters than to the generation of new minerals. Nevertheless, a few chemical and mineralogical syntheses take place. At present, these syntheses are limited to four major products which are far from occurring in all the terrigenous and pelagic sediments: on the one hand a zeolite, *phillipsite* and *manganese concretions*, both limited to a very peculiar deposit, the abyssal red clay; on the other hand, *glauconite* and *phosphatic concretions* (69), belonging specifically to green muds and green sands.

Consequently, mineral neoformation occurs in only one category of typical sediments, the green muds and green sands, since the abyssal red clay is more a chemical product than a sediment properly speaking.[56]

Before dealing appropriately with this subject, one does not expect to find such an incapacity of the submarine bottoms to generate secondary minerals. Furthermore, it should be pointed out that among the mineral productions formed today within the green muds and the green sands, only one, namely glauconite is really very widespread. The phosphatic concretions are either absent or widely scattered, without generating concentrations recalling remotely by their importance those of the geological periods.

Actually, the number of neoformations is not quite as restricted as reported by the two authors quoted above. To the glauconite and the calcium phosphate, one should add the fixation of *magnesium* in the reef constructions, starting point of the generation of magnesian limestones and dolomites; and *pyrite* which may occur in very appreciable proportion in the blue muds. At any rate, *it looks as if the bottoms covered by oozes with GLOBIGERINA, Diatoms and Radiolarians were unfit to generate mineral syntheses.* (70)

The question is now to find out if such conditions were also true in the past. It is not necessary to encompass the latter completely to find unrefutable proofs to the contrary.

For instance, the phosphatic sedimentation is completely unknown at present; yet it developed on a large scale during the different times of formation of the granular phosphorites, mainly from and including the Senonian to and including the lower Eocene. [For a discussion of Recent marine nodular phosphorites, see Editor's Introduction.] This sedimentation is the result of a chemical or biological submarine activity, the importance of which may be visualized through the vast distribution in time and space of its products.

Furthermore, a fundamental point consists in the fact that such a dispersion is far from being limited to the deposits which represent the green muds and the green sands of the geological record. The thickest, most widespread and highest grade deposits resulting from the phosphatic sedimentation, have been generated in the most typical types of oozes with Foraminifers, Diatoms and Radiolarians. In other words, *the pelagic oozes, unsuited to the development of phosphates in the present-day sedimentary sequence, displayed in the past the most favorable conditions for their generation.*[57] (71)

Consequently, anyone of these ancient oozes differs greatly from its present-day representatives. This is particularly true for the Dinantian phosphorites of the Pyrenees which consist of a pelagic ooze with Radiolarians, extremely typical by its organisms, but abnormal by its mineral composition, because of a high proportion of carbonaceous matters and calcium phosphate. Is the ancient deposit or the present-day sediment—equivalent to it by its organisms—of aberrant nature? Such a question is frequently raised when these kinds of comparisons are attempted. The answer is that in a general fashion, the sequence of present deposits is often misleading, because it displays only standards of comparison expressing a regime of great stability of the sea floor. [58]

Actually, the environments favorable to a large-scale generation of phosphates are in the geological record extremely diversified. For instance, the following types are known: phosphatic sandstones, phosphates with abundant Sponge spicules belonging to the group of the spiculites, phosphates with abundant debris of Echinoderms or with numerous valves of inarticulate Brachiopods; not to mention the phosphates with Foraminifers, with Diatoms, with Radiolarians, etc. In short, *the spectrum of phosphatic materials ranges from well characterized detrital sediments to the most typical deep-sea deposits.*

Another example, as instructive as the previous one, is afforded by the ferruginous oolites. Many ancient epochs (72) were characterized by a real *ferruginous sedimentation*, forming deposits which consisted of oolites, generated through a very complicated mineralogical evolution, and really belonging to the mineral neoformations of the submarine environment. There is not the slightest trace in the present seas of this kind of sedimentation which has generated in the past numerous iron ores. [For a discussion of Recent ferruginous oolites, see Editor's Introduction.]

Truthfully, the preceding pages give a more complete answer to the problem under discussion. Sir John Murray and Johan Hjort have stressed the fact that no *cherts* are forming on the floor of present oceans. We know from data presented above that conditions were completely different in the geological past, and that large amounts of silica, of organic origin, have been recirculated and concentrated as chert on the bottom of ancient seas. [59]

Observations of similarly striking nature have been made concerning *calcium carbonate*, showing that it may be reworked and concentrated on the sea floor, leading eventually to the formation of nodules.

CONCLUSIONS

In summary, a demonstration, based on all the necessary facts has been presented, according to which constituents of sedimentary sequences, always of essential nature such as *silica* and *calcium carbonate*, and others, essential only at certain times (73), such as *calcium phosphate* and various *ferruginous compounds*—to mention only the most important—play a fundamental role in the ancient seas, as products of mineral syntheses which have taken place during sedimentation.

It seems superfluous to exhaust the subject in order to state that a great difference exists between present and past oceans with respect to the mineral syntheses occurring in them. In order not to forget the very purpose of this investigation, one can say that *some causes which play a fundamental role in the formation of ancient sediments do not participate at all in the generation of present-day deposits.*

Whether it is possible or not to unravel the reasons for this profound difference is immaterial, the facts remain unchanged. Concerning the occurrence of the phosphatic and ferruginous sedimentation in the geological past and its absence today, its intimate relationship with ruptures of equilibrium is well known. Therefore, whenever the latter were lacking, the large-scale concentration of phosphatic materials and of ferruginous oolites appeared impossible. Since these disturbances have ceased to occur, the phosphatic and ferruginous sedimentation is unknown today. It is important to add that in the case of the oolitic iron ores, an unusual source of ferruginous material is necessary, namely the very active erosion of old mountain ranges, a process which present-day oceans cannot take advantage of.

However, in the present state of our knowledge, no satisfactory answer can be given concerning the concentrations of silica and of calcium carbonate (74) during sedimentation.

Pertaining to the cherts of the chalk, I have been trying for a long time, to understand the reason for their distribution in stringers and tabular bodies which emphasize the more or less confused stratification of the deposit, by means of the preconceived idea that their development is related to small-scale, but frequently repeated, disturbances. This question is closely related to another one, also insufficiently studied, namely the division in distinct beds of limestone deposits. In that respect, I have always been impressed by the decrease in number and even the absence of cherts within extremely fine-grained and non-stratified chalks, such as certain chalks with *M.c. anguinum* of the central part of the Paris Basin, and conversely by their abundance within the same chalks, in the region of Etretat, where the indications of instability of the sea floor are numerous.

With respect to the generation of the calcareous nodules, I do not know at present in which direction I should orient my investigations in order to explain their formation contemporaneous with sedimentation.

Regardless of the final answers concerning these two groups of rocks, the question of the mineral syntheses considered from our standpoint—and already solved—will not be modified by one iota. (75)

CHAPTER XIII

GENERAL CONCLUSIONS

The present epoch is characterized by the inactivity of a series of processes which played a great role in the formation of sediments during the geological past. This situation is due to the fact that the present is, in essence, a period of great stability of sea level and of the sea floor. Therefore, we are dealing with an exception in contrast to the geological periods considered as a whole.

The regime of the ancient seas we have investigated derives one of its typical features from the frequency of disturbances which I have designated as *ruptures of equilibrium*. This concept of ruptures of equilibrium, synonymous of far-reaching modifications of environmental conditions and of sedimentation, has been constantly repeated as leitmotif during the development of these investigations. Around them gravitate a whole series of phenomena, presently unknown, related to what I would call *Past causes*, in opposition to the *Present causes* of Charles Lyell. Is it necessary to add that these ruptures of equilibrium do not have the magnitude and the generality of Cuvier's catastrophes? They are nothing else but regional disturbances, devoid of any influence on the areas located beyond their direct action. (76)

Such disturbances unlatch new *dynamic*, *organic*, *chemical* and *biochemical* activities, which are generators of new deposits. Under their influence, the floor of the ancient seas behaves like a gigantic laboratory manufacturing various types of products, which for a long time one was inclined to attribute, either to the extended action of weathering agents, or to the intervention of mysterious springs acting on the sea

floor or during continental periods. Today it is unquestionable that the submarine environment plays a fundamental
role in the modifications undergone by sediments after their
deposition.

*These disturbances appeared, in particular, able to generate
on a large scale detrital sediments in the midst of the open
sea. They represent a necessary condition for the formation
of the sedimentary phosphorites, of the oolitic iron ores, of
almost all types of cherts, of the processes of dolomitization,
etc. They are responsible for the folding of the sea floor, the
almost instantaneous cementation of a variety of sediments,
and for large-scale submarine reworking processes, subject to
numerous repetitions.* Furthermore, we presently know that
*they have also unlatched a large bacterial activity which
seems to have played a critical role in the concentration of
sedimentary phosphorites.* [60] In my opinion, it is not
unreasonable to predict that the number of such results,
which represent only a very imperfect (77) knowledge of the
ancient sedimentary record, is bound to increase with the
progress of research.

Since these disturbances nowhere occur under our own
eyes, the spectrum of changes undergone by the recent
sediments is strongly reduced. Hence, the inadequacy so
frequently displayed by the recent processes, whenever
requested to provide data on the formation of many ancient
deposits.

Logically, we should not invoke an exception to explain
the general rule. But this is nevertheless what we have done
until today when borrowing from the present seas the
comparative data, considered necessary for the interpretation
of many ancient formations. This attitude was, by the way,
the source of countless errors. For instance, from the absence
of cherts in present deposits, one has reached the conclusion
of their late generation in the ancient rocks, whereas almost
all of the investigated cherts were formed on the sea floor.

I am not dismissing all what the oceanographers have
taught us about present-day sediments, nor despising the data
obtained from their analysis which pertain to our standpoint,

as long as we ask from them only what they can tell us, and nothing more. Obviously, their study is a rational introduction to that of ancient sediments. But it is by means of the analysis of the latter, and only through it, that we can reach an understanding of the ancient processes of the marine environment. Is this not one of the major purposes of our efforts?

On that matter, our task is not so difficult as one (78) might think *a priori*, because nature has generously put within our reach numerous examples of ancient sea bottoms which we can interrogate at leisure, after having prepared ourselves adequately for their interpretation. It is not at all preposterous to state that some of these ancient sea bottoms, although still in their initial phase of investigation, are much better known than those of present oceans. Therefore, the data obtained from the analysis of the Past Causes and of their effects should not be neglected—if it were only for the purpose of stating problems, and of contributing to establish a research program fulfilling the needs of geology—on the day when oceanographical exploration will start anew and on a much larger scale than in the past. [61]

In another field, one should not forget that the Past Causes have certainly left traces in the realm of paleontology. Unquestionably, the living conditions of marine organisms must have been deeply affected during and after each rupture of equilibrium, and at any rate these conditions were certainly different from those developed during a period of stability, as the present. We can visualize in that direction the usefulness of further investigations which might perhaps modify our ideas on many points. (79)

From the broad spectrum of data presented above and from the deductions derived from them, a leading idea clearly emerges, which I think will become of increasing importance with the progress of our knowledge:

In the study of the sedimentary formations of the earth's crust, it is necessary to take into account Past causes besides Present causes, if one wishes to use all the factors capable of providing a complete understanding of such formations.

I would not fulfill an essential duty, if I did not recall, in this conclusion, that the arguments used to justify the above-mentioned conclusion are all derived from a domain of geology completely unknown in Charles Lyell's time. Therefore, the famous author of the doctrine of the *Present Causes* should not be criticized for having misunderstood or ignored them. (80)

POSTSCRIPT

I had planned to dedicate the last year of my teaching at the *Collège de France* to a synthetical review of the particular field of geology which I have explored for almost half a century. Unfortunately, an early retirement forced upon me by the government of the *Front Populaire*, at a time when I was still contemplating three years of teaching, did not allow my project to materialize. The present study pertains only to one of the subjects which I was planning to discuss along similar lines, before taking leave from my listeners and from the famous institution to which I had the honor of belonging for twenty-five years.

L.C.

REFERENCES AND FOOTNOTES

REFERENCES AND FOOTNOTES

The footnotes in Cayeux's original text are predominantly bibliographical references to his numerous previous works—short articles and major volumes—containing the detailed field and microscopic observations on which his argumentation is based. The latter cannot be fully appreciated, and often not understood, unless such observations be readily available to the reader.

In order to overcome this technical difficulty, Cayeux's footnotes have been expanded to include not only the condensed translation of the pages he referred to, but also those of additional pages as well as abstracts of certain paragraphs which appeared indispensable for a complete understanding of his thinking. Consequently, this book is in the present form self-sufficient, being a full presentation of Cayeux's discussion and observation facts.

1. Ch. LYELL, *Principes de Géologie, ou illustrations de cette science empruntées aux changements modernes de la terre et de ses habitants.* Traduction de J. Ginestou, de la dixième et dernière édition, 1873, Paris, Garnier Frères, vol. I, p. 115, La première édition de l'ouvrage, en deux volumes, date de 1830 et 1832.

Twelve editions of the "Principles of Geology" were published in England until 1875, and many of them were reprinted in the United States. The word "dernière édition" for the tenth edition is a common mistranslation for "latest edition".

The above reference as given by Cayeux is incomplete by being only part of one of the statements given at the beginning of Chapter V entitled "Prejudices which have retarded the progress of geology", p. 90, and summarizing its content. The full statement reads as follows: "Objections to the doctrine that causes similar in kind and energy to those now acting, have produced the former changes of the earth's surface, considered." (*Principles of Geology or the modern changes of the earth and its inhabitants considered as illustrative of geology*, 1867, tenth and entirely revised edition, 2 volumes, London, John Murray).

As early as 1825, Constant Prévost assumed that the causes of present processes did not differ essentially from those active during geological time. A few years later, the concept of similar intensity of past and present forces became one of the fundamental tenets of the theory of present causes.

The first account of Prévost's ideas in 1825 is as follows: "The author, using as an example some of the youngest deposits of the Paris Basin, proposes to demonstrate that the assumptions based on the present state of nature, and therefore not contradicting in any way the laws of general physics, are sufficient to explain the formation of the great variety of deposits which build the most recent layers of the earth. The observations of Mr. C. Prévost have led him to the following fundamental idea: around us, either on the surface of the land, or under water, or within and around volcanoes, phenomena occur whose causes are not essentially different from those which, at different times in the past, have successively shaped the various geological conditions of the globe. It is before having observed all the effects of the causes still active at present, and having compared them step by step to effects produced in the past, that several famous geologists have stated that all past natural processes were different from present ones. Everyday experience shows, on the contrary, that soft and very hard beds, as well as coarse and very crystalline deposits are still being formed; that natural solvents of a large portion of the substances dissolved in the past still exist today; that petrifications, and consequently fossils are being formed today, etc."

"If the investigation of the various changes which have occurred at the surface of the globe demonstrates a continuous gradation between its present state and the past condition—when as a planet its relationships with the other celestial bodies were established as we know them today—then it should not be necessary, when explaining the geological facts, to require the intervention of extraordinary causes which could only act at present by disturbing the universal order . . ."

"Assuming that the study of what happens today in the ocean basins and particularly in a well-defined basin could—by means of the philosophical method of proceding from the known to the unknown, and from the simple to the complex—afford useful data on the origin of deposits which have recently emerged from the waters in which they were formed . . . Mr. C. Prévost develops a lengthy comparison between the present-day environmental conditions of the English Channel, near the mouth of the Seine, and the past depositional environment of the Cretaceous and Cenozoic beds of the Paris Basin."

"Mr. C. Prévost presents this comparative work as a typical example of the use of the analytical method in geology. In his opinion, numerous mistakes could have been avoided and science would have progressed much further if the study of ancient sediments had not started before the observation of present nature. It is only since the geologists have carefully examined the most recent layers of the earth's crust and compared the organic remains they contain with the organisms living at present . . . that a new period of positive discoveries began." (De la formation des terrains des environs de Paris: *Bull. Soc. Philomatique de Paris*, 1825, S. 3, vol. 12, pp. 74-77, 88-90)

In 1845, after the appearance of Lyell's publications, C. Prévost further developed his concept of uniformity, presenting the opinion that the forces responsible for ancient phenomena, were not only comparable in nature, but also equivalent in intensity with those presently active. He wrote as follows: . . . . "The study of present-day phenomena and its application to the explanation of past ones have finally demonstrated as an unquestionable truth, the synchronous action since the remotest times, of two major causes: the plutonian and the neptunian."

. . . "Nothing indicates in good geology and sound logics that complete creations have been suddenly destroyed by universal catastrophes, after which they were miraculously replaced by new creations."

. . . "We can almost state that when the oldest rocks containing the earliest traces of organized beings were deposited, the earth and its surface already displayed conditions similar to those of the present; that fossil plants and animals did not, by their organization, differ from living plants and animals; that present organisms could have accomodated themselves to the external condition of the earth at the time of the Late Paleozoic."

"Mr. C. Prévost announces two other memoirs, one of which will demonstrate that present geological phenomena act on a similar scale as they did in the past; and that the effects which are produced or could be produced today by extraordinary but possible events, are not and would not be smaller in extent, magnitude or intensity than those displayed by the geological column considered, for instance,—to avoid any appearance of exaggeration—as far back as the Carboniferous." (De la chronologie des terrains et du synchronisme des formations (extrait): *C.R. Acad. Sc. Paris*, 1845, vol. XX, pp. 1062-1071)

On this subject of uniformitarianism in the proper sense, one would read with great profit—as pointed out by Cayeux himself—lecture eight entitled: "Des causes en géologie" in the book of Ch. Sainte-Claire Deville: *Coup d'oeil historique sur la Géologie et sur les travaux d'Elie de Beaumont*, 1878, Paris, G. Masson, pp. 205-221.

2. The expression of "ancient causes" is borrowed from the *Principles of Geology* by Ch. Lyell who wrote several pages under the heading of "assumed discordance of ancient and modern causes" (Ginestou's translation, vol. I, pp. 130-135; tenth edition, chapter V, pp. 102-105).

It seems appropriate to quote here the original text of Lyell (pp. 104-105): "The establishment, from time to time, of numerous points of identification, drew at length from geologists a reluctant admission, that there was more correspondence between the condition of the globe at remote eras and now, and more uniformity in the laws which have regulated the changes of its surface, than they at first imagined. If, in this state of the science, they still despaired of reconciling every class of geological phenomena to the operations of ordinary causes, even by straining analogy to the utmost limits of credibility, we might have expected, at least, that the balance of probability would now have been presumed to incline towards the close analogy of the ancient and modern causes. But, after repeated experience of the failure of attempts to speculate on geological monuments, as belonging to a distinct order of things, new sects continued to persevere in the principles adopted by their predecessors. They still began, as each new problem presented itself, whether relating to the animate or inanimate world, to assume an original and dissimilar order of nature; and when at length they approximated, or entirely came round to an opposite opinion, it was always with the feeling, that they were conceding what they had been justified *a priori* in deeming improbable. In a word, the same men who, as natural philosophers, would have been most incredulous respecting any extraordinary deviations from the known course of nature, if reported to have happened *in their own time*, were equally disposed, as geologists, to expect the proofs of such deviations at every period of the past."

"I shall proceed in the following chapters to enumerate some of the principal difficulties still opposed to the theory of the uniform nature and energy of the causes which have worked successive changes in the crust of the earth, and in the condition of its living inhabitants."

3. L. CAYEUX, Contribution à l'étude micrographique des terrains sédimentaires: *Mém. Soc. Géol. Nord*, 1897, vol. IV, 2, pp. 324-326.

Calcium phosphate of the chalk with BELEMNITELLA

QUADRATA in the southeast part of the Paris Basin and major characteristics of that chalk.

. . . The predominant characteristic of this formation is the presence of calcium phosphate. Since this substance occurs in appreciable amount in each of the investigated zones, except in the upper one where the content decreases, its distribution throughout an important thickness of the chalk belonging to the base of the formation can be reasonably assumed. If sedimentation had not been more active in this particular region (S.E.) of the Paris Basin than at the locations of the deposits of phosphatic chalks with *Belemnitella*, in other words, if the same amount of phosphatic material had been concentrated throughout a thinner column, this question might have attracted attention since long ago. The most critical feature is represented by an important generation of phosphate within a chalk containing an extremely small amount of detrital minerals and in a region which should be considered, by definition, as protected from any shoreline influence. In this particular case, it is extremely difficult to account for the mode of accumulation of the phosphatic components, if we accept the idea of A.F. Renard and J. Cornet (Recherches micrographiques sur la nature et l'origine des roches phosphatées (Notice préliminaire): *Bull. Acad. roy. Belgique*, 1891, Ser. 3, vol. 31, pp. 126-161) that the grains were formed near the coastline and subsequently transported into deeper waters. This last episode of the history of the grains assumes an increase of mechanical activity. Therefore, why do the constituents associated with the phosphates not show any trace of it? Although I have observed an increase in the number and the diameter of the detrital minerals, such differences are certainly not commensurate to those which would imply an increase of the power of transporting agents, capable of displacing grains of calcium phosphate reaching a size of 1 mm or more. Perhaps the difficulty could be avoided by assuming that among the mineral constituents, some were transported by surface currents and others by bottom currents. The phosphate grains would belong to the second case and the other detrital

particles to the first. Actually, this assumption is a poor
answer to the problem. If the phosphatic constituents were
generated in littoral waters and subsequently transported
down into the deeper portions of the Cretaceous sea, they
should be associated with large quartz grains and with
products of the comminution of organisms such as debris of
Inoceramus tests, which would have followed the same path.
The investigated chalk shows absolutely nothing peculiar in
that respect. Therefore, the conditions favorable to the
generation and accumulation of the phosphatic grains have
had no influence on the constitutive elements of the chalk. It
looks as if only the chemical agents which participate in the
genesis of this deposit had been modified. Truly, the opinion
of a generation of the grains *in situ* or near their places of
accumulation—although unexplainable at first glance—seems
more in agreement with the features of the enclosing chalk
than the idea of their generation outside the region of their
present occurrence. Actually, in this particular problem, the
interpretation of A.F. Renard and J. Cornet disagrees only
with the facts concerning the place where the phosphatic
granules are formed. If we consider that they were generated
not in littoral zones but in areas where only a small number
of detrital particles could penetrate, it would be much easier
to explain why the detrital minerals associated with the
phosphate grains are not more numerous and of larger size.
The existence of bottom currents leaving traces of their
activity far away from the shores of the Cretaceous sea is
sufficiently demonstrated to leave no difficulty in explaining
the transportation and the accumulation of large phosphatic
grains generated away from the shores . . .

The major characteristics of the composition of the chalks
with *Belemnitella* are as follows:

A. In a mineralogic viewpoint, the most interesting features
besides the occurrence of calcium phosphate, glauconite and
vermicular kaolinite (leverrierite) are: *a.* pseudomorphic
replacement of Sponge spicules by calcium phosphate; *b.*
partial or complete crystallization of the cement into
isolated, irregularly-shaped and juxtaposed rhombohedra.

B. In an organic viewpoint: *a.* occurrence of relatively numerous Sponge spicules (nodular chalk) characterized by very thick and large forms; *b.* reappearance at the base of the formation of a great number of large Foraminifers with arenaceous test; *c.* increase of the size and thickness of the test of all the Foraminifers at the base of the formation; *d.* completely different content of organisms between the areas of phosphatic chalk and of normal chalk; *e.* occurrence of Radiolarians.

The examination of the minerals and organisms of the base of the formation points toward an appreciable diminution of the depth of the sea at the beginning of the Campanian.

Ibid. id., pp. 427-432.
General results of the study of the chalk of the Paris Basin
The secondary minerals—Calcium phosphate
. . . Calcium phosphate, amorphous or crystallized, occurs in all types of chalks. . . I have observed previously described types of grains, such as fragments of bony tissue, constituents resulting from the filling of the internal cavities of Foraminifers, and microscopic concretions. I have also demonstrated the occurrence of a new type of grain which I think is of great importance for the history of that mineral. It is completely independent from the other types of grains, and has been generated *in situ* to the same extent as the associated microscopic concretions. . .

Among the different unsolved questions pertaining to the formation of the phosphorite deposits of the chalk of France is the process of *accumulation* of the phosphatic granules which generated the large concentrations in the chalk of Northern France and the vicinity of Mons. . . . A.F. Renard and J. Cornet (*op.cit.*, p. 157) visualize the origin of the phosphatic chalk as follows: "During the Cretaceous, a chalky mud was deposited even along the shoreline itself. As in the present—day *Globigerina* oozes, the phosphatic matters, produced by the accumulation of the residues of the littoral fauna, infiltrated the shells of the chalky mud. Therefore, the molding of the phosphatic components took place near the shores, and subsequently, *currents, tides and waves transported them toward the open sea.*"

Objections against the hypothesis of the transportation of phosphate grains from the coasts toward the open sea.

Numerous objections may be raised against this process of transportation of the phosphate grains. Any mechanical action capable of transporting phosphatic grains of one or several tenths of a millimeter in size, should also affect the *mineral* and *organic* components occurring in the sediment where the phosphatic granules are generated.

1. The phosphate grains, although of *higher density* than those of quartz, are *invariably* accompanied by quartz grains of a size smaller than .1 mm.

N. de Mercey (Remarques sur les gîtes de phosphate de chaux de la Picardie: *Bull. Soc. Géol. France*, 1891, Ser. 3, vol. 19, pp. 860-861) demonstrated that the phosphate grains of the chalk with *B. quadrata* have the following size-distribution:

15 % have a diameter greater than .5 mm

25 % have a diameter equal to .25 mm

60 % have a diameter smaller than .2 mm.

In conclusion, *the phosphate grains are not sorted*, and their size is appreciably larger than that of the quartz grains.

2. The number and the size of the detrital components of the phosphatic chalk with *Belemnitella*, for example, compared with those of the nonphosphatic chalks among which it is interbedded, should display a very appreciable increase since the deposition of the phosphatic chalk would have been characterized by the intervention of mechanical actions having not affected the other zones. I have yet to see such a difference where the very fine-grained white chalk with *M.c. anguinum* grades into the phosphatic chalk with *Belemnitella*. When glauconite is so abundant in sedimentary rocks that a process of transportation is required to explain its accumulation, one can invariably observe that the associated quartz is also affected. For instance, if the size of the glauconite grains increases, that of the quartz becomes also larger. In summary,

in this particular case, nothing may be observed which would indicate *a behavior of the calcium phosphate independent of the detrital constituents of the chalk*.

3. Why did not currents, waves and tides transport, together with the phosphate grains, numerous large debris resulting from organic activity, such as *Inoceramus* prisms and other shell fragments? This is not easily understood, particularly since the dynamic action of the water was capable of breaking up vertebrate bones.

4. It is similarly difficult to understand why along a coast where water was agitated, detrital minerals should be so few and so small.

5. Another very important question, of paleontological nature, should be raised. Currents, tides and waves carry toward the open sea phosphate grains which predominantly consist of easily recognizable Foraminifers in spite of their phosphatic envelope and filling. But, in the waters toward which they are transported, another fauna of Foraminifers occurs which has distinct characters, different from those of the fauna which invades its domain. One group characterizes agitated littoral waters, the other open sea conditions. As of now such an association has never been observed, and I have not seen any feature which might even suggest its occurrence.

In my opinion, the proof of the transportation of the grains from littoral regions to deeper zones will not be obtained until the coexistence of two distinct faunas of Foraminifers will be shown within the deposits of phosphates; one essentially of littoral character as required by the hypothesis of A.F. Renard and J. Cornet, the other corresponding to the deeper areas, farther away from the coasts, and toward which the former fauna would be transported.

6. The Foraminifers enclosed within the phosphatic grains are intact. If, in the Paris Basin, the conditions of sedimentation had been as postulated in general by A.F. Renard and J. Cornet, many shells should have been broken to a variable degree, and their chambers dissociated. Furthermore, grains containing Foraminifers, at different stages of destruction, should occur.

7. A last objection is provided by the distribution of the deposits of phosphates with *Belemnitella* in the Paris Basin. H. Lasne (Sur les terrains phosphatés des environs de Doullens, étage sénonien et terrains supèrposés: *Bull. Soc. Géol. France*, 1890, Ser. 3, vol. 18, pp. 486 and fol.) assumed in 1890 that the calcium phosphate of the Somme originated from the Central Plateau of France, had been transported in solution across the entire basin by surface currents originating from the south, and eventually precipitated at its present places of occurrence.

In 1892, E. Munier-Chalmas (Origine des phosphates de la Somme et formation de la craie: *C.R. Somm. Soc. Géol. France*: 1892, Ser. 3, vol. 20, pp. XLVII-L), relying on the existence of currents coming from the north which I had demonstrated the previous year by means of the behavior of the detrital minerals and the pebbles of the chalk, presented the opinion that the phosphate originated from Scandinavia. Let us consider successively the ideas of currents coming from the south and the north and their consequences if these currents were in turn responsible for the transportation of completely formed phosphatic grains.

The first hypothesis appears immediately unrealistic, because the south-east part of the Paris Basin is, among the regions I have investigated, that which displays the least traces of any dynamic action of the water. How can one explain the extreme rarity as well as the very small size of the detrital materials in a chalk which has received from the coast, and for a long period of time, numerous grains of calcium phosphate reaching one or several tenths of a mm in size? I just cannot accept this hypothesis. *The introduction of phosphatic matter in the chalk with* BELEMNITELLA *of the Yonne coincides neither with an appreciable increase of the insoluble residue, nor with a larger size of the extremely rare detrital constituents.* Therefore, the hypothesis is as follows: currents, tides and waves transport numerous phosphate grains and nothing else, and the submarine area which receives such an influx appears completely undisturbed by such an important event. I can hardly see how such different circumstances could be conciliated. I would like to add that the existence of currents coming from the south is hypothetical for the entire Paris Basin, except for the south-west, and it is even more so for the Yonne in particular.

If currents coming from the north are assumed, the interpretation of the transportation of completely formed phosphatic grains becomes even more difficult. Nobody would consider the hypothesis of having the phosphate grains move across the entire basin to reach the Yonne, since the chalks extending north of the Yonne, and which should have been affected in some way by the passage of the current, display a perfectly normal composition.

In summary, the hypothesis of the genesis by transportation of the calcium phosphate of the Yonne presents enormous difficulties regardless of the direction chosen for the source-area of the grains.

As early as 1892, H. Lasne (Sur les terrains phosphatés des environs de Doullens, étage sénonien et terrains superposés, 2ème note: *Bull. Soc. Géol. France*, 1892, Ser. 3, vol. 20, p. 217), on the basis of the size of the phosphate grains, had been led to consider the transportation of the phosphate, visualized by A.F. Renard and J. Cornet, a mechanical impossibility.

New explanation for the generation of the phosphate deposits of the chalk of the Paris Basin

I wish to point out concerning the hypothesis of A.F. Renard and J. Cornet, the unquestionable fact that some of the grains have been generated *in situ*. These two scientists themselves had to recognize a *duality of origin* of the phosphatic constituents in order for their theory to account for all observed properties. They assumed that the *nodules* were formed *in situ* ... Consequently, some phosphatic matter has been transported in solution toward the places where the deposits occur. I have been able to demonstrate that in the Nord in particular, numerous grains have been formed within the chalk in which they presently occur; the microscopic concretions which result from the partial or total replacement of small portions of the chalk are also abundant;

and megascopic nodules are not rare. In other words, a rather appreciable proportion of the calcium phosphate has been formed directly *in situ*.

With respect to the large deposits such as those of Aisne, Oise, Pas-de-Calais and Somme, a transportation of the grains could be accepted, but in the light of a new interpretation.

The generation of calcium phosphate at the base of the chalk with *Belemnitella* represents a rupture of equilibrium of the Cretaceous sea which can be easily demonstrated by the following features:

1. Cementation of the top of the chalk with *M.c. anguinum*, extending downwards as far as one meter beneath the phosphatic chalk.

2. Perforations extending through the cemented upper part.

3. Phosphatic coating over the shells attached to the top of the chalk with *M.c. anguinum* along its contact with the phosphate; a feature indicating an interruption of sedimentation.

4. The strange development of Corals reported by J. Gosselet (Des conditions dans lesquelles s'est fait le dépôt du phosphate de chaux en Picardie: *C.R. Acad. Sc. Paris*, 1896, vol. 123, p. 290; Note sur les gisements de phosphate de chaux d'Hem-Monacu, d'Etaves, du Ponthieu: *Ann. Soc. Géol. Nord*, 1897, vol. 24, pp. 109-134), beneath the phosphatic chalk at Hem-Monacu, near Péronne. This fact indicates an appreciable change of the marine environment.

5. Erosional features, also recognized by J. Gosselet in the white chalk with *Micraster* before the deposition of the phosphatic chalk of Hem-Monacu.

6. Finally, the changes of thickness of the tests of Foraminifers (Somme and Yonne) which imply a biological change due to *shallower waters*.

This rupture of equilibrium has particularly affected certain parts of the Basin, by uplifting them, and by generating small valleys corresponding to the strange depressions of phosphatic chalk discovered by H. Lasne. The phosphatic constituents were generated over such areas, temporarily submitted to depth conditions recalling those of shorelines. The phosphate was first precipitated directly as a brown shiny coating, consisting of calcium phosphate almost chemically pure, over the upper surface of the chalk with *M.c. anguinum* and over the fossils which lived on top of that chalk during the period of interruption of sedimentation. The great majority of the phosphatic grains was deposited subsequently. *Nothing has been changed with respect to the relationships between these particular places and the shoreline; detrital minerals were brought to them in the same proportion as before.* The phosphatic grains may have undergone displacements *on the sea floor* to be eventually accumulated in the areas of greatest slope, but for the Yonne in particular, these displacements are not required.

This new but hypothetical explanation suppresses the objections raised against the theory of A.F. Renard and J. Cornet, not concerning the generation of the grains, but their local concentration in very rich deposits. The required bathymetrical conditions are compatible with those which seem necessary to J. Gosselet for explaining the different features of the deposits of phosphorites of the chalk of France. . .

Relationship between the deposits of phosphorites of the Upper Cretaceous of the Paris Basin and the great ruptures of equilibrium of the Cretaceous sea.

The occurrence of the deposits of phosphorites of the Paris Basin appears very closely related to the ruptures of equilibrium of the sea. Such a relationship is of great importance to explain the *physical* and *chemical* conditions under which these deposits were formed.

1. The phosphatic chalk of the Département du Nord is related to an uplifting which made the sea recede from the embayment of Mons. Its occurrence is related to a period of marine *regression* for the Nord.

2. The phosphatic chalk with *Belemnitella* corresponds to the great Campanian *transgression*.

3. That of the Basin of Mons is contemporaneous with the *regression* of the sea in the Paris Basin after the deposition of the white chalk with *Belemnitella*.

4. I could quote another unusual example without leaving the Paris Basin: the phosphate of the Artois (Pernes) which corresponds to the great Cenomanian transgression.

Two deposits are related with regressions, two others with transgressions. Regardless of the nature of the relationship between the formation of phosphorite deposits and the great displacements of the sea, the following law may be stated for the Paris Basin: *all the Upper Cretaceous deposits of phosphorites were generated at times of great ruptures of equilibrium of the sea.*

L. CAYEUX, Phosphates sénoniens du Bassin de Paris, *in* Les Phosphates de chaux sédimentaires de France: *Etudes Gîtes Min. France, Serv. Carte Géol. France et des Top. Sout.,* 1939, vol. I, pp. 202-259.

This volume is an exhaustive description of the Senonian phosphorites of the Paris Basin as well as an elaborate discussion of their conditions of formation. Only excerpts related to the question of past and present causes and complementing the preceding reference will be given here.

Cayeux divided his treatment of the subject as follows:
1. Phosphatic chalks and sands.
2. The coarse materials forming the base of the phosphatic chalk.
3. The cherts of the phosphatic chalk.
4. The substratum of the phosphatic formation and its modifications.
5. The pockets of phosphatic sands.
6. The movements which affected the sea floor, before, during, and after the deposition of the phosphatic chalk.
7. General considerations.

The coarse materials forming the basal part of the phosphatic chalk consist of abundant nodules; from those of the deposit of Fresnoy-le-Grand, Cayeux has reached the following important conclusions (pp. 224-226):
1. The nodules consist of fragments of several types of chalk, playing the role of *imperfect pebbles*. They are generally rounded, subangular or irregularly-shaped bodies with superficial irregularities not smoothed out by abrasion. This

situation confirms Gosselet's idea of their local origin. Furthermore, they are randomly distributed within the deposit.

2. The only materials associated with the nodules-pebbles are numerous organic debris, such as fragments of *Inoceramus*, shark teeth, etc. *with the absolute exclusion of any constituent foreign to the chalk*. Once more, *it looks as if the relationships with the emerged land had undergone no change*.

3. The search for the source-rocks of the materials of the basal conglomerate tends to show that only two formations have contributed to the process: first, the underlying chalk with *M.c. anguinum*, and to a much lesser degree, the chalk with *M.c. testudinarium*. . .

4. These nodules-pebbles, after their formation, have been perforated, and often several times. They have obviously reached their final place of deposition through successive stages, corresponding to different areas of the sea floor and to sediments of variable nature. These conditions are clearly demonstrated by the different types of filling displayed by the perforations. A close examination reveals that to each type of filling corresponds a time of perforation, because if all the perforations of a given nodule were of the same age, how could their filling by such a variety of materials be visualized? These complex environmental conditions appear, for the time being, unique in the history of ancient sediments.

5. In many nodules, the process of perforation has been followed by the development of organic incrustations and of a concretionary coating of phosphate which seal off the openings of the perforations at the surface. This coating consists of a superposition of very thin laminae of pure phosphate, pale yellow and crystalline, recalling, although on a larger scale, the envelope surrounding the grains of phosphatic chalk. The different organisms attached to the surface of the nodules are enclosed within the phosphatic chalk itself, which above them is in general reduced to several millimeters or even to a fraction of a millimeter. Regardless

of their size, these nodules are completely incrusted by organisms, but their envelope of concretionary phosphate is continuous all around them and responsible for their shiny aspect. All these facts indicate that the nodules were maintained in suspension in a saturated or supersaturated solution.

6. Whether we are dealing with reworked fragments of chalk variably phosphatized, or with perforations, the question of the cementation of the fragments should be raised. This problem does not exist for the fragments provided by the substratum which had reached a high degree of cementation before the beginning of the phosphatic sedimentation. But these fragments represent only a portion of the reworked materials. The fact that the others are also of irregular shape, even angular, that their surface has not even lost its irregularities, demonstrates a very high degree of cementation, since it is well known that a single tide is sufficient to shape a piece of clay into a perfect mud ball. The occurrence of angular splinters, broken off from the chalk of the nodules, along the margin of certain perforations, is also an argument in favor of such a concept of early cementation.

Numerous observations to be discussed later in detail (see Chapter XI and footnote 50) demonstrate that the sea floor which generated the phosphatic chalks, has undergone movements—for a long time unsuspected—which created folds with very small radius of curvature, the most developed being asymmetrical, isoclinal, overturned and even recumbent. These structural features represent details of the foldings with large radius of curvature which affected the chalk of the Paris Basin.

The general conclusions reached at the end of this reference are essentially the same as those presented by Cayeux in 1897, but are now amplified.

The formation of the phosphatic chalk appears to require the following succession of processes. Its beginning coincides with a great rupture of equilibrium foretold by embryonic movements. This disturbance separates the chalk with *M.c. anguinum* from the chalk with *Belemnitella*. Its first effect is to interrupt sedimentation, then to appreciably modify and even to erode the upper part of the chalk with *M.c. anguinum*. It is quite possible that the rupture of equilibrium may have led to local emergences. However, the generation of the coarse materials of the base of the deposit, does not afford any data for or against this possibility. *If such were the case, we would be dealing with an emergence occurring in open sea, and in the opposite situation with a succession of submarine processes, including the generation of the coarsest conglomerates.*

At the same time, according to the observations of H. Lasne and J. Gosselet, little ridges occurred on the sea floor and their development generated a very complex submarine topography which displayed in particular the depressions in which the phosphatic materials were transported and concentrated . . .

It is appropriate to recall here that the generation of the phosphatic chalks, as that of the oolitic iron ores, implies the existence of two entirely distinct environments, one where grains and nodules are formed, the other where the phosphatic materials, carried away from their generating center and reworked, are finally concentrated. Right or wrong, *I consider the high points of the sea floor, located in the open sea and under bathymetrical conditions recalling those of shorelines, to be precisely the generating centers of the phosphatic materials.* Very agitated waters and currents attack these high places endlessly, fragmenting the chalky mud—undergoing cementation or having been already cemented—and therefore generating numerous debris. From these particular areas the small and large phosphatic constituents, completely formed, are removed and transported toward the adjacent depressions. Favorable conditions are continuously renewed because movements contemporaneous with deposition of the phosphatic chalk, emphasize the submarine reliefs. If the phosphatic materials were filling the depressions by themselves, extremely rich deposits of phosphatic sands would result. But since the entire basin is located in the open sea, a very fine chalky sedimentation, similar to the one which everywhere else forms the white chalk with *Belemnitella*, occurs at the same time in these depressions. The typical phosphatic chalk results from the intimate mixture of phosphatic grains and chalky mud. At times, the currents play a predominant role and grains are brought into the depressions in such a great amount that the deposit is a thin bed of phosphatic sand interbedded between two layers of phosphatic chalk . . . Conversely, the great predominance of the chalky sedimentation explains the occurrence within the phosphatic chalk of inclusions, lenses or even banks of normal chalk. Then quiet conditions gradually become predominant, the phosphatic grains decrease in number and the phosphatic chalk grades into the white chalk. Occasionally the change of sedimentation may be abrupt, after a paroxysm of the mechanical agents which generates very rich phosphatic chalks at the top of the formation. Although cyclical repetitions may also occur, the phosphatic episode always ends with the return of the pure chalk sedimentation.

4. L. CAYEUX, Contribution à l'étude micrographique des terrains sédimentaires: *Mém. Soc. Géol. Nord*, 1897, vol. IV, No. 2, pp. 431-432.
5. L. CAYEUX, Phosphates sénoniens du Bassin de Paris, *in* Les phosphates de chaux sédimentaires de France: *Etudes Gîtes Min. France, Serv. de la Carte Géol. France et des Tops. Sout.*, 1939, vol. I, p. 205.

In general, the phosphatic formation builds a *single layer*, in other words, the phosphatic sedimentation continued uninterruptedly during early Campanian times, generating a single and unique concentration. At Curlu, near Péronne (Somme), I have reported for the first time, in 1890, the occurrence of three distinct phosphatic beds separated by the white chalk with *B. quadrata* where only the upper bed had undergone a partial decalcification. In the same region, at Hem-Monacu and according to J. Gosselet, wells have encountered four layers of rich phosphatic chalk, separated by white or yellowish-white chalks, always slightly phosphatic. The deposits of Etaves (Aisne) and of Haravesnes (Pas-de-

Calais) display a double phosphatic formation. Actually, these repetitions are few and the concentration of the phosphatic chalk in a single bed must be considered as the general rule with only rare exceptions.

6. L. CAYEUX, Contribution à l'étude micrographique des terrains sédimentaires: *Mém. Soc. Géol. Nord*, 1897, vol. IV, No. 2, p. 432.

7. L. CAYEUX, Les minerais de fer oolithique de France. II. Minerais de fer secondaires: *Etudes Gîtes Min. France, Min. Trav. Publics*, 1922, p. 935.

8. L. CAYEUX, Les minerais de fer oolithique de France. II. Minerais de fer secondaires: *Etudes Gîtes Min. France, Min. Trav. Publics*, 1922, pp. 629-630.

9. L. CAYEUX, *op. cit.*, p. 446.

10. L. CAYEUX, Contribution à l'étude micrographique des terrains sédimentaires: *Mém. Soc. Géol. Nord*, 1897, vol. IV, No. 2, pp. 480-483.

In the chalk of the Paris Basin, Foraminifers, frequently not the essential constitutents, have undergone at least two large-scale—and at first glance unsuspected—destructive actions. The first one is a mechanical fragmentation in the environment of deposition; the second is a destruction after deposition by recrystallization. In both cases, Foraminifers have contributed by their partial or total destruction to the generation of the cement of the chalk. Therefore, the original organic composition of the chalky mud has been deeply modified and to an extent which remains unknown. Fortunately, several substances have locally preserved these organisms, giving an idea of the magnitude of the transformations undergone by the rock. These substances are: *clay minerals, calcium phosphate* and *silica*. The different circumstances of the preserving action of these substances remain to be established, but they must certainly pertain to the physical factors such as porosity, capillarity, etc., which regulate the processes of cementation. In the case of the argillaceous chalks, the scattered clay minerals seem to generate a more compact texture which protects the shells of Foraminifers by reducing the circulation of waters saturated with CO_2. For a given length of time, the amount of CO_2 brought in contact with the organisms enclosed in an argillaceous chalk is smaller than for an almost entirely calcareous chalk. Therefore, their chances of destruction are reduced.

The *partial* replacement of a chalk by phosphate has led to the preservation of numerous shells which have disappeared from the non-replaced portions. This situation is well demonstrated by the phosphatic chalk with *Belemnitella* from the Yonne and the Somme. In the latter, in particular, the Foraminifers which appear concentrated in the phosphatized areas are partially or completely excluded—within the same thin section—from those not replaced by the phosphate. There is no doubt that their distribution was originally uniform.

Furthermore, these phosphatic zones display organisms as Radiolarians which are missing in the surrounding chalk, and are even very rare in the chalk of Europe in general. They occur concentrated, sometimes in appreciable number in a very small area and abruptly disappear outside the phosphatized areas. It seems very unlikely that the location of the phosphatic areas had been originally characterized by the occurrence of Radiolarians, and that none of them existed within the chalky patches entirely surrounded by the phosphatic chalk.

All the data seem to indicate that the original distribution of these organisms was uniform, as that of Foraminifers, and that their complete absence outside the phosphatic zones results from the processes which have deeply modified the original aspect of the chalk . . . In summary, it seems clear that in order to visualize the content in organisms of the chalk when it was accumulating as a mud on the sea floor, the phosphatized portions should be investigated. These reveal to us the fundamental fact that *the chalks, displaying today very few organisms, were originally foraminiferal muds, and that Radiolarians most probably played an appreciable role in the organic composition of the chalky mud*. It is partially by means of the preserving properties of the phosphate that we can reconstruct the original condition of the chalky ooze and visualize at a single glance the magnitude of the change it has undergone to reach the stage of a chalk characterized by a low content of microorganisms.

The chalky dust enclosed within the hollow cherts shows a much greater proportion of perfectly preserved microfossils (often silicified) than the surrounding chalk. The conclusion may again be reached that the latter has lost an appreciable amount of microorganisms, and that *the content of the hollow cherts indicates the original organic composition of the chalk*. The chalk within the cherts becomes, therefore, a kind of standard reference for comparison with the surrounding chalk in order to establish the sum of all the changes its content of organisms has undergone.

Organisms are not only more abundant in the chalk enclosed within the cherts than in the surrounding one, but their state of preservation is also much better. These conditions obviously indicate that the formation of the cherts preceded the cementation of the chalk.

11. J. MURRAY and A.F. RENARD, Deep Sea Deposits in *Rep. of the scient. results of the exploring voyage of H.M.S. Challenger during the years 1873-1876*: 1891, Pl. XX, fig. 2-4.

12. L. CAYEUX, Les phosphates de chaux sédimentaires de France: *Etudes Gîtes Min. France, Serv. de la Carte Géol. France et des Tops. Sout.*, 1939, vol. I, pp. 143-154, Pl, VI, fig. 18, 19.

This reference pertains to the phosphatic nodules of the Albian green sands with *D. mamillare*. They are heterogeneous nodules with a smooth or mammillated surface, grayish to greenish-brown on the outside, dark brown to black inside. Most frequently they are scattered throughout the sands, but may be occasionally welded together to a variable extent forming a kind of conglomerate . . . These nodules consist essentially of three components: quartz, glauconite and a cement of calcium phosphate. Organisms, mainly Sponge spicules and Foraminifers, occur in a greatly variable proportion, and frequently are missing.

Whenever detrital quartz is abundant, the nodules consist actually of a glauconitic sandstone with a phosphatic cement. The glauconite displays three major aspects: lobate grains of detrital nature as quartz and older than phosphatization; pigments within the phosphate and contemporaneous with it; and a last stage, later than phosphatization, in which glauconite has replaced calcium carbonate apparently along veinlets of calcite filling contraction cracks of the nodules. Pyrite is almost always present, replacing phosphate. The perfect preservation of most of the fossils enclosed in the nodules indicates that phosphatization took place during sedimentation, and immediately after the deposition of the organic debris on the sea floor. The phosphatic cement displays a variable degree of crystallinity, and often contains inclusions of calcite and clay minerals, indicating that the original matrix was calcareo-argillaceous.

Two interesting features characterize many of these nodules: a generalized process of fissuration and a particular kind of reworking.

Fissuration has led to nodules consisting of two completely unrelated phosphates. For instance, some nodules collected on the beach of Wissant, appear fractured throughout their entire thickness. The picture suggested by their transverse fracturation is that of a body cracked at random as a clay undergoing desiccation. Occasionally, some cracks, reaching 3 millimeters in width, have remained open. In general, however, they are filled by a variety of substances among which three predominate: pyrite, calcite and a fine-grained matter, of pale gray color which resembles more a sediment than a mineral. In the present state of our knowledge, the nodules of the green sands of Wissant display the highest degree of fracturation and at the same time the greatest variety of filling materials. In those from La Hève, the cracks forming a network of large lattices are filled by a single and homogeneous matter intimately welded to the main mass of the nodule. Some nodules from the Ardennes display a similar feature which, therefore, becomes very widespread among the green sands of the Paris Basin.

The fillings of the cracks by pyrite or by calcite are not of particular interest in comparison with the third type of filling, of sedimentary aspect and unquestionably related to the surface of the nodules. Thin sections show thin bands of this material, perfectly individualized by means of their color and particular composition, extending throughout some nodules. Two examples will be sufficient to state a problem which seriously complicates the history of the phosphatic nodules of the green sands.

1. A nodule from La Hève, cut through the middle, displays a network of a few polygonal lattices, reaching about one centimeter in diameter and outlined by narrow gray-blue bands, more than half a millimeter wide and intersecting each other. Under the microscope, these narrow bands consist of calcium phosphate devoid of any glauconite grains and of the largest quartz grains which are however abundant along their margins. On the contrary, Foraminifers occur in these bands in greater abundance than in the rest of the nodules. Glauconite and quartz grains appear sharply truncated along the margins of the narrow bands and their missing parts are never found within such narrow bands.

2. A second type of occurrence, belonging to the Albian nodules of the beach of Wissant, shows irregularly branching veinlets which stand out by being either lighter or darker colored than the nodule itself. Inside these veinlets, quartz and glauconite may be concentrated or completely missing, but in both cases the composition of the filling perfectly distinguishes the veinlets from the groundmass to the extent that their pattern is always clearly displayed. Furthermore, Foraminifers are again more abundant in them than in the rest of the nodule.

A very glauconitic nodule from Saulce-Montclin (Ardennes) is intersected by a phosphatic vein, totally devoid of glauconite.

In all the observed cases, *there is, so to speak, an intimate interpenetration of two different phosphates which, as soon as the cracks reach a certain minimum width, behave as two completely unrelated rocks.* Obviously, these nodules, once formed, have undergone a contraction process, important enough to generate a system of large cracks. The fundamental feature, however, is the fact that the network of cracks has been filled, at a certain time, by a matter mineralogically and organically different from that of the nodules. Therefore, the following conclusions may be reached:

1. The fissuration of the nodules is a submarine process.

2. The degree of cementation of the nodules was already very advanced when fissuration took place. This condition is demonstrated by the grains of glauconite and quartz located along the margins of the cracks which, instead of being broken loose from the rock, have been truncated by the fracture planes.

3. Entirely different producing environments correspond to the two generations of calcium phosphate which characterize the history of such nodules; in other words, these nodules have been reworked and transported to areas of the sea floor very different from those which generated them.

4. In general, the transportation has taken place in the direction of the open sea, a conclusion supported by the decrease in number of the detrital minerals, the smaller size and greater abundance of the Foraminifers.

A few nodules furthermore enclose smaller ones independent of them in all respects, and such a situation implies the reworking of the small nodule enclosed in the larger one. Nodules incrusted with materials which are different from those which generated them are also of great interest. For instance, the surface of a nodule from the green sands of La Hève displays incrustations consisting of a glauconitic limestone with Foraminifers and devoid of quartz, which is certainly not the parent-rock of a quartzose nodule containing very few Foraminifers. Another nodule from La Hève shows, in a few places, coatings of a calcareous and phosphatic rock, very glauconitic, and in sharp contact with the nodule itself which contains very little glauconite and abundant quartz. The microscopic picture looks like two very different rocks juxtaposed. In both instances, the residues of matrix attached to the nodules demonstrate that the latter did not remain in the environment which generated them . . . In conclusion, the concentration of nodules in layers occurring at different levels within the green sands results from a mechanical distribution. In other words, these concentrations are comparable to conglomerates.

13. *Ibid. id.*, pp. 183-186, Pl. VII, fig. 22 and 23.

Evidence of submarine reworking displayed by the Cenomanian phosphate nodules of Pernes-en-Artois and of the chalk of Rouen.

1. *Nodules of Pernes-en-Artois.*

These nodules, as those related to the Albian green sands, show large well-defined streaks, very different from their main groundmass. Some of these streaks consist of a phosphate containing a very small number of glauconite and quartz grains, entirely devoid of organic debris and of a completely different shade, for instance gray, within a straw-yellow groundmass. The contrast between the two juxtaposed phosphates is extremely sharp. As in the case of the Albian nodules, the fissuration of the nodules and the filling of the cracks seem to have occurred in a sedimentary environment different from the one in which they originated. In other words, these nodules have been reworked on the sea floor.

Another fact, of equal significance, leads to the same conclusion. Thin sections cutting across the glauconitic chalk and the enclosed nodules display differences which are incompatible with the idea of a simple phosphatization *in situ*. On one side, the chalk contains numerous large grains of glauconite and is therefore a typical glauconite rock with very few quartz grains; abundant debris of bony tissue; broken *Inoceramus* prisms; many thin-shelled Foraminifers, and a very small amount of matrix. On the other side, the nodule is quartzose, contains very little glauconite, numerous Sponge spicules, but is devoid of *Inoceramus* prisms, Foraminifers and fragments of bony tissue. Could one visualize a more striking contrast between juxtaposed portions?

Furthermore, the same thin section shows submicroscopic nodules. One of them contains few Sponge spicules, while another is completely devoid of them but displays abundant quartz grains, always with the exclusion of *Inoceramus* prisms, Foraminifers and fish remains.

2. Nodules from the chalk of Rouen

The glauconitic chalk of Rouen affords very interesting data pertaining to the problem discussed here. Within a single thin section cutting across three small phosphatic nodules and their matrix, the following facts may be observed:

The matrix is a coarse-grained chalk containing an equal proportion of glauconite and of calcium carbonate, very few Foraminifers, no Sponge spicules and a moderate number of small quartz grains. The grains of glauconite are large, irregularly-shaped, generally mammillated, and always devoid of organic shape. Not a single Foraminifer is invaded by glauconite.

The largest of the three nodules, reaching a maximum diameter of 11 millimeters is different in all aspects from the chalky groundmass. Indeed, it contains numerous Sponge spicules, monaxonic, cigar-shaped, cylindrical, intact or broken and replaced by glauconite. These spicules are completely absent in the chalk. Furthermore, the large grains of glauconite are missing, quartz is rare, and Foraminifers— predominantly *Textularia*—occur with a certain frequency, but in general have a relatively thin and calcareous test. The matrix is undifferentiated pure phosphate, straw-yellow in color, enclosing numerous small calcareous residues. It is difficult to visualize a more striking contrast between associated materials.

The second nodule differs from the preceding one by a smaller content of Sponge spicules, the occurrence of numerous glauconite grains as large as those of the chalk, but of a different shade, and by the abundance of remains of Foraminifers which have become essential constituents. They consist predominantly of small individuals of *Globigerina* and *Orbulina*. Some of them display concentrations of glauconite in their chambers, but in general the tests have only undergone an incipient corrosion. Many Sponge spicules however have been phosphatized.

The third nodule differs from the two others mainly through the great abundance of Foraminifers which are the major constituents. It derives from a chalk with *Globigerina*, containing a few Sponge spicules and some glauconite grains, smaller and of slightly different color than those of the matrix.

Between crossed nicols, the calcium phosphate of all three nodules appears predominantly, if not entirely, crypto-crystalline.

One of the nodules is particularly noteworthy by the occurrence and frequency of glauconitic veinlets. In that respect, it may be unique among the phosphorites of France. It shows irregular veinlets which are simple, bifurcated, branching, continuous or discontinuous, and occasionally extending throughout the nodule. All the mineral and organic constituents are injected by glauconite, except quartz. Whenever the veinlets encounter grains of glauconite, or spicules replaced by glauconite, the two juxtaposed varieties of glauconite have different structures and shades. Observations are sufficient to show that the veinlets never extended outside the nodules . . .

On the basis of the preceding data, it seems possible to understand the major features of the history of the Cenomanian phosphatic nodules of the Paris Basin. Four major facts are obvious:

1. All the investigated nodules together with their chalky matrix indicate a generating environment different from that in which the nodules presently occur. The comparative analysis of the associated constituents shows that the difference between the environments could have been very pronounced. In other words, all the nodules are reworked, and many indicate a reworking process of great magnitude.

2. Not only has reworking taken place, but the phosphatic nodules associated within a single fist-size specimen have different origins, a conclusion reached through the analysis of a glauconitic chalk of Rouen and of Pernes-en-Artois.

3. This reworking may be double as shown by the nodules intersected by veinlets and streaks of material different from their main mass. In other words, *their history implies the intervention of three distinct environments: A. The original generating environment; B. The environment in which the*

filling of the cracks has taken place; C. The environment of final deposition of the nodules in the chalk.

4. Certain nodules originate, as shown by their mineralogical and organic features, from an environment more distant from the shorelines than that of the enclosing chalk. This situation is demonstrated, for instance, by the following facts: the grains of glauconite and of quartz contained in the nodules are much smaller and less numerous than those of the chalky matrix; the Foraminifers of a given nodule have a subpelagic character which is never that of the surrounding chalk. Apparently, some nodules—in a proportion which cannot be established—originated from the open sea. A last important feature of the nodules is the extreme rarity and often the absence of fragments of bony tissue.

In conclusion, the history of the Albian and Cenomanian phosphatic nodules of the Paris Basin is similar in many fundamental aspects.

14. J. MURRAY and A.F. RENARD, *op. cit.*, p. 397.

15. L. CAYEUX, Les "boulets calcaires" de la formation phosphatée du Bassin de Gafsa (Tunisie) et les enseignements qui découlent de leur étude: *C.R. Acad. Sc. Paris*, 1939, vol. 208, pp. 1951-1953.

The phosphatic formation of the Gafsa Basin is characterized petrographically by the occurrence of numerous *"boulets calcaires"*. This designation is applied by the miners to constituents of greatly variable size and generally of rounded shape, but which have two distinctly different modes of occurrence.

Some of them, by their size and morphology, are closely related to nodules, commonly called *"miches"*. Limestone beds enclosed within the non-productive zones of the phosphatic complex, grade along strike into stringers of flat, lenticular blocks, reaching 1 meter or more along their greatest axis and are occasionally transitional to bodies which look like large pebbles. The generation of such constituents is usually explained by a segregation of the calcium carbonate within a marly environment. In other words, these nodules belong to the large group of the *concretions*.

The history of the materials of the second group is completely different because they unquestionably represent typical *pebbles*. They occur without exception in an isolated fashion, often widely separated from one another, but always at particular stratigraphic levels. These may be used as key-beds in the phosphate as well as in the non-productive beds.

The following example, taken from the excellent section of the Oued Lousif, at Metlaoui, gives a good picture of the phosphates with "*boulets calcaires*". The two mined beds and the intermediate non-productive unit reach a total of 7 meters thickness. Eight zones of *boulets* occur throughout this thin sequence, and many more could be added if the entire formation were considered.

Two stringers of large *boulets*, related to the non-productive intercalation, grade laterally into lenticular beds without any trace of reworking. In that respect, they clearly appear as stringers of *miches* (*cordons de miches*).

The *boulets* of the six other stringers belong to the group of true pebbles. Those forming the upper stringer of the laminated phosphatic "marls", enclosed between the two mined beds, are particularly typical. They appear as perforated pebbles, oriented at random, and ranging in size from a few centimeters to 20 or 30 centimeters. Some have been so abraded that their original shape cannot be recognized, others are still sub-angular. Most of them display a very smooth and polished surface of waxy appearance as if they had been covered by a coating of unknown thickness. Several flat pebbles have been perforated over their two major faces. Others of rounded shape have been perforated all around and to such an extent that no residue of the original surface remains. The largest, and at the same time the most common perforations have the same average size as those of Pholads. They occur by themselves or associated with small superficial perforations ranging from a fraction of a millimeter to several millimeters in diameter and are locally extremely abundant. Generally, the perforations have been filled by calcium phosphate. There are flat pebbles whose two plane faces have

apparently been perforated in slightly different environments, as demonstrated by the occurrence of different filling
products on both sides. The state of preservation of the
margins of the perforations demonstrate that some pebbles
have been reworked and abraded after having been deeply
perforated.

Among the problems presented by the *boulets*, two are
particularly interesting in a genetic viewpoint.

1. *Time of formation of the MICHES.*

This question was raised earlier by similar bodies related to
the iron ores of Lorraine (L. Cayeux, Les minerais de fer
oolithique de France. II. Minerais de fer secondaires: *Etudes
Gîtes Min. France, Min. Trav. Publics*, 1922, fig. 23, p. 445,
see also footnote 26). The gray bed, in particular, may
contain in great abundance, calcareous nodules occasionally
of large size. Their relationship with the ore demonstrates a
formation *in situ* by a process of concentration of the
calcium carbonate. Furthermore, some of these nodules,
located in the upper part of the gray bed, have been
truncated by the overlying limestones with ferruginous
oolites. These facts prove that the important erosion undergone by these nodules could only have taken place on the sea
floor, and that they were already formed when the deposition of the gray bed ended. In summary, we are dealing with
a process of formation penecontemporaneous with
sedimentation.

The same conclusions hold true for the *miches* of the
Gafsa Basin, as shown by the occurrence of organic perforations in the upper part of certain *miches*. Therefore, their
differentiation results unquestionably from a submarine
process, and did not follow emergence.

2. *Parent-rocks of the BOULETS CALCAIRES.*

The limestones of the non-productive intercalations, the
limestones of the discontinuous beds displaying the facies of
miches, and the numerous *boulets* which are true pebbles
show a very pronounced petrographic similarity. All three are
light-gray limestones, sometimes as fine-grained as the finest

chalk. Some are extremely pure, being devoid of either phosphate or quartz, others display from a few to several hundred phosphatic grains in a single thin section. Organic remains are very rare and almost always debris of *Globigerina*.

The relationship between these rock-types is such that all the reworked limestones, changed into true pebbles, derive, without exception, from the phosphatic complex. If the complete absence of reworked materials, other than the *boulets calcaires*, is taken into account, the following conclusion may be reached: *the phosphatic formation, throughout its deposition, has been the only source of the enclosed coarse-grained constituents.* This striking example deserves to become classical in the study of the reworking processes which take place on the sea floor, without intervention of any emerged land.

The study of the *boulets calcaires* is similarly instructive for the investigation of the processes of submarine cementation. It reveals that the limestone beds, intercalated in the phosphatic complex, have immediately acquired a sufficient cementation to be converted into pebbles of all sizes, shaped by the dynamic agents to the extent of being perfect without ever having been broken . . .

If the concepts derived from these observations have no longer the characters of novelty, they have nevertheless the advantage of affording particularly striking arguments in favor of some of the leading ideas I have previously presented.

16. L. CAYEUX, The phosphatic nodules of the Agulhas Bank (A study of submarine geology): *Ann. South African Museum*, 1934, vol. XXXI, pp. 105-136.

This submarine bank was at the time of Cayeux's investigation the only sizeable area of concentration of abundant phosphatic nodules as opposed to the scattered occurrences dredged during the oceanographic expeditions of the *Challenger, Blake, Gazelle* and *Valdivia*. The Agulhas Bank was furthermore of great interest for a comparison between recent and ancient phosphate deposits.

The major aspects of the paper are as follows:

External characters of the nodules.

The nodules collected from the Agulhas Bank have a striking morphology, seldom comparable to that of the pebbles of the Albian greensands of France. Their shape is extremely variable in detail, generally rounded, but occasionally very angular. The nodules are furthermore mammillated, provided with protuberances, even deeply indented, and perforated by numerous holes. They may be divided into two groups. The majority are characterized by an irregular form and range in color from blackish-gray to pure black; the others are angular and brownish-yellow. The former are dull, and the latter have a highly polished and varnished appearance. In other words, one group resembles concretions, while the other suggests reworked rock fragments. Some of the latter show large cavities associated with tiny perforations filled with glauconite. These differences of facies do not appear to be related at all to the bathymetric conditions where the nodules have been dredged, except that the lightest colored nodules were found at depths of 192 and 421 meters, while the blackish ones were dredged from 281 to 731 meters.

Many nodules carry organic incrustations, mostly due to Bryozoans which extend either over their whole surface—proof that the nodules have been rolled in every direction—or cover only one portion. Several nodules are completely devoid of incrustations.

The nodules whose largest diameter does not exceed 7.5 cm are either isolated or cemented into a true conglomerate, apparently by an interstitial matrix which consists of a variably consolidated greensand. It should be pointed out that, regardless of their shape, the nodules have acquired the consistency shown by the hardest pebble of the Albian of the Paris Basin.

Chemical composition of the nodules

Chemically, the nodules of the Agulhas Bank belong to the category of low-grade phosphates, but the phosphoric acid content is of the same order as that of the Albian greensands of the Paris Basin.

Petrographic classification of the nodules
The following six varieties may be distinguished in a petrographic viewpoint:

1. *Very quartzose calcareo-phosphatic nodules*

These blackish nodules display the highest content of detrital minerals of all investigated types. Quartz, representing on the average less than 50%, is very uniform in size and evenly distributed. Glauconite is relatively rare. The fauna consists of a few *Globigerina*, and the calcareo-phosphatic matrix is sparingly developed. This rock is certainly far from being a typical greensand.

2. *Very glauconitic, phosphatic or calcareo-phosphatic nodules with GLOBIGERINA.*

These nodules are blackish and incrusted with glauconite which also fills perforations. Glauconite largely predominates over detrital quartz. It is very irregularly distributed, completely absent in some places and elsewhere forming the greater part of the groundmass. The *Globigerina* are widely scattered since very little cement is present. All transitions occur between this type of nodule and the preceding one.

3. *Calcareo-phosphatic nodules with Bryozoans and PULVINULINA.*

In these nodules of very deep color, quartz is less abundant and glauconite rather rare. Bryozoan fragments are numerous, while *Globigerina* are considerably reduced in number and replaced by thick-walled individuals of *Pulvinulina*. The amount of matrix has also increased, and this type of nodule is very distinct from the preceding ones.

4. *Quartzose calcareo-phosphatic nodules with abundant GLOBIGERINA.*

These nodules differ greatly from the preceding ones by their buff-yellow color. Detrital quartz is not so frequent as in the first two types, while glauconite has become an accessory mineral. The principal feature of this type is the abundance of *Globigerina* and the presence of spicules of calcareous Sponges. The interstitial matrix is very unimportant, although it can be considered as a transitional term to the true *Globigerina* mud.

5. *Phosphatic and ferruginous nodules with GLOBIGERINA.*

These nodules of angular shape and brown color are almost free of quartz, very poor in glauconite, and particularly rich in *Globigerina*. Their phosphatic and ferruginous matrix has preserved the organisms in a beautiful fashion and many of them are riddled with perforations filled with iron oxide. All types examined, this kind of nodule displays the greatest affinity with the *Globigerina* ooze.

6. *Phosphatic and ferruginous nodules with large benthonic Foraminifers and Bryozoans.*

The organic remains of these nodules are in reciprocal contact and lead to a very coarse aspect in thin section. They consist of benthonic Foraminifers with extremely thick tests, fragments of Bryozoan colonies, plates and spines of Echinoderms, fragments of tests of Mollusks and Brachiopods. Rare pelagic forms such as *Globigerina*, sometimes arranged in rows, may also occur. Most of the organisms are riddled with perforations filled with calcium phosphate and iron oxide. Detrital minerals and glauconite are entirely missing. The matrix of calcium phosphate and iron oxide plays a very important role both in the fossilization of the tests and in the infilling of the cavities.

Another type should be added, differing greatly from the six former ones and consisting of nodules of phosphatic greensand. This type is replicated in the nodules made up of two different lithologies and will be described under that heading.

The phosphatic nodules of the Agulhas Bank display a great petrographic variety, ranging from terrigenous types, such as the very quartzose calcareo-phosphatic nodules, to the phosphatic and ferruginous ones with *Globigerina* which resemble pelagic formations. All intermediate terms occur between these extremes. The variety characterized by Bryozoans and numerous benthonic Foraminifers appears to represent one end of the spectrum. It illustrates an example of the numerous organic deposits formed in terrigenous environments which never occur in true pelagic sediments.

All these phosphatic nodules have been dredged from a bottom of *greensand*, and the specimens which most closely approach a *Globigerina* ooze—although differing by a very small amount of detrital quartz—have been recovered at a depth of only 192 m., that is well outside the actual domain of the *Globigerina* oozes.

In conclusion, no deposit of phosphates in the ancient sedimentary record contains such a variety of petrographic types, nor raises such an important problem.

Analysis of the constituents of the nodules.

Detrital quartz is always angular and has a mean diameter of less than .10 mm; therefore, nearly all the grains would float in weakly agitated water. The variations in size and frequency of the quartz grains are independent of the depth at which the nodules were dredged. Glauconite displays a great variety of occurrences: rounded grains with often internal zones of oxidation; replacement of a variety of organic debris—including Foraminifers—with filling of internal cavities; abundant matrix in pigmentary form, and finally minute veinlets, similar to those observed in Albian nodules. At least two generations of glauconite have to be considered; first the free grains and the filling and replacement of organic debris, second the epigenetic glauconite of the matrix and of the veinlets.

The very rare Sponge spicules observed are calcified. This situation proves that the solution of siliceous spicules and their replacement by calcite are not necessarily late processes following the emergence of the sediments. The *Globigerina* show no corrosion and their fragmentation must be due to mechanical actions.

On the basis of the composition of the matrix, the nodules may be divided into two distinct groups: the blackish and the brownish. The matrix of the blackish nodules recalls that of the phosphatized chalks of the North of France. Although little developed because of the abundance of Foraminifers, it is generally calcareo-phosphatic and the phosphate has usually replaced the calcium carbonate to a limited extent. The brownish nodules are far from displaying a constant type, calcium phosphate is more abundant in them and often associated with iron oxide. The organic remains, both pelagic and benthonic Foraminifers, are corroded and commonly the carbonate portions which have escaped replacement show a crystalline condition comparable to that of the highly recrystallized ancient limestones.

Anomalies of composition and structure of the nodules.

Some of the dark colored nodules which originate from quartzose *Globigerina* muds are characterized by inclusions and incrustations of aberrant composition, others by the juxtaposition of two very dissimilar rocks.

1. *Nodules with very glauconitic inclusions*

In these nodules glauconite forms narrow, well-defined bands, devoid of minerals and organisms. These bands differ from the grains of glauconite included in the main mass of the nodules by a light brownish color. This same variety of glauconite may cement large grains of glauconite, different again from those within the nodules. Thus we are dealing here with two generations of glauconite which are completely unrelated in time with those described in the nodules of normal type. Other types of inclusions are rich in grains of ordinary glauconite set in a cryptocrystalline phosphatic cement devoid of microfossils.

The two above-described types of inclusions sharply cut across any constituents of the main mass of the nodules along straight or irregular lines. In three dimensions they clearly represent longitudinal or transverse sections of complex cavities filled by greensands. Therefore, we are dealing with an interpenetration of two fundamentally distinct types of rock: an older, atypical *Globigerina mud*, and a true *greensand*, both consolidated. The same contrast exists between the material of the nodules and their mineral incrustations which do not differ at all from the inclusions and bands.

Under these conditions, the unescapable conclusion is that *the nodules formed at the expense of atypical* GLOBIGERINA *muds, have been removed from the locality in which they were formed and deposited in areas where greensands were being laid down.* This conclusion leads to another one: *During this process, the nodules have been transported from a sediment which is more pelagic than terrigenous into another typically terrigenous one, and from greater depths to more shallow areas*

Nodules formed by two different lithologies.

In the case of nodules consisting of the juxtaposition of two different rocks, the two portions appear separated by a darker line, .05 mm thick. For instance, the lower portion of such a nodule consists of a yellowish limestone containing debris of Bryozoans, Echinoderms, and a small amount of Foraminifers, mostly *Globigerina*. The carbonate matrix of the rock displays quartz and glauconite and is replaced by calcium phosphate. The intensity of this replacement increases toward the contact of the two rocks. The partial alteration of the glauconite accounts for the yellow color of the rock. The fact that this alteration does not extend to the glauconite of the upper part of the nodule—of more recent formation—shows that it is an ancient process of submarine origin.

The dark zone which marks the upper limit of the lower rock is characterized by an intimate association of calcium phosphate and pigmentary glauconite from which calcium carbonate has completely disappeared. Glauconite also occurs as anastomosing veinlets and as a replacement product of all the organic debris which elsewhere are perfectly preserved. There is no encroachment of the phosphatized limestone above this zone which appears sufficiently irregular to be called a *line of corrosion*.

The upper rock is coarse-grained and contains more quartz and glauconite grains. The size of both minerals indicates a strongly agitated environment. The matrix consists of crypto-crystalline gray to yellow calcium phosphate free from fine calcareous inclusions and showing a few fragments of bony tissue. This rock is similar to that which forms by itself the nodules of phosphatized greensands and has been briefly mentioned together with the six major types. It also resembles very closely certain pebbles of the greensands with *D. mammillatum* from the east of the Paris Basin.

These composite nodules show the effects of a great submarine disturbance which produced an erosional surface. Two fundamentally different rocks are in contact, one derived from greensands and the other from a Bryozoan-foraminiferal limestone; two deposits formed in contrasting environments. The composite bodies are actually rocks detached from a contact between two distinct formations and shaped into nodules, or more properly into pebbles.

The phosphatic nodules of the Agulhas Bank raise also the question of *submarine corrosion*. The deep penetration of the glauconite of the greensands into certain nodules on one flat side or over their entire surface clearly indicates that corrosion has affected materials already separated from the parent-rock, in other words, the nodules themselves. All the corrosion unquestionably precedes the penetration of the greensands into the cavities it generated, however, corrosion continued after the change of environment which caused the greensands to appear because the phosphatic greensand forming the upper part of the composite nodules is also corroded.

The question is far from elucidated because an unknown proportion of nodules, such as those produced from green-sand, has escaped corrosion.

Nomenclature

The term nodule has been used until now in this text because it does not imply any given mode of origin, while that of *concretion* immediately suggests concentration around one or several points of attraction. Among the materials from the Agulhas Bank, the only true concretions are the phosphatic greensand nodules. All the other bodies result from a process of replacement of calcium carbonate by calcium phosphate, a mechanism which does not obey the same laws as the former, and which is moreover quite independent of their morphology.

In summary, *all the phosphatic materials of the Agulhas Bank, without exception, are nodules and an unknown fraction of these nodules falls within the category of concretions.*

Interpretation of the facts.

The above-mentioned facts, such as the great variability at a given location of the brownish nodules, which range from a consolidated *Globigerina* mud to a deposit with benthonic Foraminifers and debris of Bryozoan colonies, indicate a *submarine reworking.* Indeed, these two very different rocks could not have been formed at the same depth. The existence of vuggy nodules with *Globigerina* containing inclusions devoid of these tests, and the nodules consisting of two distinct rock-types, represent further evidence along the same lines. Furthermore, the latter nodules introduce the idea of *submarine erosion* coinciding with a drastic change of environmental conditions. *This erosional process has acted on the calcareous substratum in the same way as the changes of sea depth of the Upper Cretaceous on the chalky muds of the Paris Basin: cementation of the sea floor, impregnation by phosphate and by glauconite, etc.*

All the reworked material is derived from deposits which were formed at a greater depth than that at which they were dredged. Everything points toward an uplift of the sea floor of great amplitude, which has raised up limestones of varied types, and even *Globigerina* oozes. This change of level, of the order of magnitude of hundreds of meters, has terminated the deposition of limestones, started the formation of greensands, and induced the processes of erosion, disintegration, transportation, corrosion and re-cementation of the materials. Phosphatization also belongs to this complex association of processes whose equivalents in the distant past always occur in connection with great environmental changes.

This variation of sea-level with its consequences can explain the *duality of origin* of phosphatic rocks. At the same time as the pre-existing materials were undergoing replacement, true concretions were also being formed at the expense of the greensands. This accounts for the association of true pebbles and concretions which occurs likewise in more ancient phosphorites. The petrographic variety of the pebbles found in a single place could be explained by the fact that they were dredged along the external steep slopes of the bank. It can be assumed that the different types of limestone, from which the phosphatic nodules have been derived, crop out in horizontal beds on the slopes of the plateau which itself is covered with a very thin mantle of greensands. Regardless of the stratigraphic succession of the deposits, it is natural that, following the change of depth, a concentration of nodules would be produced on the outside talus of the bank. Furthermore, one can suppose that this surface, deeply eroded during uplifting, would enable the dredge to explore different zones of the complex forming the Agulhas Bank.

Whether this interpretation is acceptable or not, *the phosphatic nodules of the Agulhas Bank are unquestionably not dependent on present-day phenomena*. This conclusion is possibly too absolute. It applies to all the nodules which do not result from the consolidation of greensands as well as to the nodules formed of two rocks welded together, one of which was derived from phosphatized greensand. Actually, one can show that the nodules formed from replaced limestones are not of modern origin, but such a demonstration is not possible for the concretions exclusively formed within consolidated greensands.

Whatever the age of the phosphatic deposits of the Agulhas Bank, the major phosphatization which produced them unquestionably began before the present epoch and after the disturbance which put an end to the deposition of limestones and replaced them by greensands. The change of level is of such magnitude that it probably occurred before the Pleistocene.

All the above data indicate *that the submarine deposit of the Agulhas Bank constitutes so to speak the last phase of an important sequence of phosphatic sediments which are distributed almost from one end to the other of geologic time.* As much as is known at present, this deposit reveals no essential difference from the older phosphatic formations.

If one separates the phosphatic nodules of the Agulhas Bank from those of the present because they are older—with the reservation made above concerning those solely derived from greensands—the distribution of modern phosphates becomes very restricted . . . and throws but little light on the vast problem of the genesis of sedimentary phosphorites. To find a solution it is necessary to pin our faith on the past.

17. L. CAYEUX, Le Gothlandien du sondage de Danneville (Calvados), et son milieu générateur: *Livr. Jub. Cent. Soc. Géol. Fr. 1830-1930*, 1930, vol. I, pp. 197-212, Pl. XXVII and XXVIII.

The interest of this drilling lies essentially in the sequence of predominantly ampelitic shales intersected between 263.20 m and the depth of 333.15 m where it was abandoned. The sequence consists of very ampelitic and pyritic shales, often replete with Graptolites, in which thin beds and nodules of limestone—reaching at the most 10 cm thickness—and a few sandstones are interbedded at irregular intervals. In addition to the abundant Graptolites, individuals of *Orthoceras* are very numerous at certain levels, as well as *Cardiola interrupta*. Cubical pyrite is extremely widespread, often concentrated in nodules and small lenses, and occasionally replacing the tests of all the megascopic organisms including *Orthoceras*.

The limestones interbedded within this shaly sequence will be described from a mineralogic and organic viewpoint because of their great interest for paleo-oceanography.

The limestones

The limestones, intimately associated with the ampelitic shales, display very uniform megascopic features. Their color is dark gray, blackish, or even black, and the fracture surface always dull. The bedding planes separating the limestones from the shales often display numerous and well-preserved worm tracks. Furthermore, one particular limestone bed, at a depth of 284 m shows an erosional surface with a relief reaching 2 centimeters.

Most of these limestones contain enough carbonaceous matter to be designated as *ampelitic limestones.*

Under the microscope, the coloring pigments consist of an association of carbonaceous matter largely predominant over pyrite. In transmitted light, the two components are difficult to separate from each other except for the fact that pyrite has a tendency to occur as well-defined elements, such as crystals, grains and granules reaching an average size of .04 mm. Whenever the pyrite individuals are welded to each other, they still preserve a certain particularity never displayed to the same degree by the carbonaceous matter. In reflected light, the separation of the two constituents is very easy, the brilliant gray-yellowish reflection of the iron sulphide contrasting with the black and dull aspect of the carbonaceous elements. The use of reflected light shows that the frequency of the pyrite is, in general, inversely related to that of the carbonaceous matter.

The carbonaceous matter appears normally as a real framework of variable density enclosing calcareous elements and organisms which display aberrant conditions of fossilization. The carbonaceous matter, whenever largely predominant, builds a black opaque background in which are scattered irregularly-shaped calcareous constituents and organic debris, not always identifiable, but among which numerous small arcuate forms, aligned parallel to bedding, are certainly Ostracodes. Whenever reduced to a minimum, this framework becomes discontinuous and loose, and eventually changes either into thin black coatings around the calcareous constituents, or into vague dark clouds within the calcium carbonate. In a few rare instances, the carbonaceous matter forms thin, discontinuous laminae extending throughout a given thin section.

The calcareous mass which includes all the inorganic components consists of irregularly-shaped grains, with an average size of .10 mm, and giving no clues about their origin. In general, the calcium carbonate tends to be largely crystallized with single optical orientation being almost the rule. Only the largest individuals appear twinned.

The carbonaceous matter surrounds the carbonate components to a variable extent and gives the impression of corroding them marginally, although this might be an illusion. Furthermore, this matter invades them as hair-like lines and as an extremely fine and often very dense dust which interferes with their limpidity. Only within some of the organic debris does the calcium carbonate escape this invasion by the carbonaceous matter. The association of these two substances seems to indicate a simultaneous origin. Exceptionally, the calcite forms numerous rhombohedra and small subrhombohedral grains enclosed within a very carbonaceous matrix. Finally, the calcite may display a very aberrant feature by replacing gypsum crystals.

The insoluble residue of the limestones shows minute quartz granules, invisible in thin sections. Therefore, the emerged land provided the ampelitic limestones with only a very negligible amount of detrital minerals. Their size is so small that the source-area could be extremely far away.

The organic components consist of *Orthoceras*, abundant tests of Ostracodes, calcitic or replaced by carbonaceous matter, rare rodlets attributed to Sponge spicules, and numerous Radiolarians entirely replaced by the carbonaceous matter with only their general morphology preserved. Some calcareous Algae may also be present locally. The observed fauna does not include a single representative of the Foraminifers, Echinoderms, Brachiopods or Bryozoans; hence benthonic forms are almost completely excluded. Furthermore, those Radiolarians sufficiently preserved to be identified, have very delicate tests indicating predominantly surface types. In summary, almost all the identifiable organisms are planktonic.

Aberrant types of ampelitic limestones

Two types are of fundamental importance:

1. *Limestone with calcified gypsum crystals.*

This particular limestone, one centimeter thick and encountered at a depth of 285.40 m, appears replete with
microscopic crystals of calcite which are obvious pseudomorphs after gypsum. Most are lenticular, while the others
have distinct monoclinic shapes and grade into the former by
means of all intermediate shapes. These crystals are identical
except for their smaller size to those of the lagoonal
Cenozoic of the vicinity of Paris, and particularly to those of
the *silex nectiques* of the zone of Saint-Ouen (Seine). (See
L. Cayeux, Introduction à l'étude pétrographique des roches
sédimentaires: *Mém. Carte géol. France*, 1916, p. 276, Pl.
XVI, fig. 3; *Ibid.*, Les roches sédimentaires de France. Roches
siliceuses: *Mém. Carte géol. France*, 1929, p. 669, Pl. XXIX,
fig. 117. For a description of the *silex nectiques*, peculiar
kinds of cherts associated with evaporites, see A.V. Carozzi,
Microscopic Sedimentary Petrography: 1960, John Wiley and
Sons Inc., New York, p. 339)

These crystals reach an average size of .05 mm and a
maximum of .07 mm. Mineralogically, most of them are
characterized by single optical orientation, but a few differ
by the occurrence of insignificant patches of calcite with
different orientations and scattered at random throughout
the single crystal.

The matrix of this unusual rock, totally devoid of organic
debris, consists of an association of cryptocrystalline calcite,
clay minerals and abundant carbonaceous pigments. Because
of the great interest of this rock, interbedded within a
sequence of strong pelagic character, I should stress that the
identification of *calcified gypsum* is beyond any doubt. The
thousands of observed crystals could not, by any means, be
interpreted as the products of decomposition of the pyrite,
present in all ampelitic limestones because the shape itself of
the crystals excludes such an origin. Besides, pyrite never
shows any tendency toward alteration.

In summary, the Upper Silurian with Graptolites of Normandy affords the unrefutable proof of evaporation processes represented by the deposition of a bed of gypsum. The unique character of this lagoonal episode remains to be proved.

2. *Limestone with calcified crystals of quartz and feldspars.*

At two different levels, 297 m and 305 m, ampelitic limestones contain megascopic crystals, isolated or in patches, with shapes similar to those of feldspars and quartz. The former have stubby forms and often interpenetrate each other, while the latter are generally free and rather elongate. Both minerals, with one exception, have been replaced by aggregates of calcite. This only exception is a clear feldspar crystal with fine cleavages and calcified only along a regular and marginal band .08 mm wide.

I have no idea about the conditions of this process of calcification of feldspars and quartz. The partially replaced feldspar excludes the possibility of solution cavities subsequently filled with calcite. Perhaps the diabase eruptions of the area could be related to these neoformations. At any rate, the process has not affected the preservation of the organisms, because thin and perfectly preserved Ostracode shells occur near patches of replaced feldspar crystals.

General considerations

The composition of the investigated ampelitic limestones raises several fundamental questions. The first one pertains to the large-scale concentration of the animal or vegetable organic matter on the sea bottom and its role in fossilization processes. The second question relates to the unusual mineralogical aspects of these rocks, namely: large-scale generation of cubical pyrite; complete elimination of the silica of the Radiolarians without leaving any trace in form of cherts; complete calcification of gypsum crystals; generation of numerous crystals of feldspar and quartz followed by their calcification.

However, the most important question concerns the generating environment of these rocks which is not in agreement with presently held concepts. The picture of the investigated area during the Gothlandian is that of *an extremely shallow sea, characterized by an exceptionally rich plankton which receives from the shoreline only negligible clastic materials, and is capable of generating evaporites.*

After all, this set of conditions—one would not expect associated within the same formation—can only be developed in open sea, as demonstrated by the type of fauna, the insignificance of continental influx, the abundance of limestones with respect to the other occurrences scattered westward in the direction of the Atlantic continent and in a general way by all the features of the investigated sediments.

Therefore, both the episode of lagoonal evaporation corresponding to the deposition of gypsum and the erosional surface mentioned above are located in open sea conditions. In order to visualize such a situation, we must assume local processes in waters so shallow that a very small rupture of equilibrium is sufficient to create a lagoonal environment over a restricted area and lead to the erosion of a bed just deposited.

The abundance of carbonaceous matter fits the idea of shallow waters, so does the occurrence of a fauna of Radiolarians. Their delicate test is characteristic of a typical pelagic fauna, adapted to quiet waters. These conditions are otherwise necessary for the accumulation of the Graptolites and do not at all imply a great depth. The almost complete absence of benthonic organisms indicates that bottom conditions in that sea were improper and even occasionally lethal to life.

There is no reason to believe that such environmental conditions were exceptional, and a general study of the Gothlandian ampelitic deposits may lead to some interesting results concerning the oceanography of that period.

18. *Ibid. id.*, Pl. XXVIII, fig. 7.

19. L. CAYEUX, Introduction à l'étude pétrographique des roches sédimentaires: *Mém. Carte géol. France*, 1916, Atlas, Pl. XVI, fig. 3.

20. G. Mantell, a British scientist, was the first, in 1822, to report the occurrence of chert breccias in the chalk. However, he did not draw any conclusion regarding the time of formation of the cherts (G. MANTELL, *The Fossils of the South Downs*; or *Illustrations of the Geology of Sussex*: 1822, London, L. Relfe, p. 147).

21. L. CAYEUX, Les roches sédimentaires de France. Roches siliceuses: *Mém. Carte géol. France*, 1929, p. 583-604.

It is appropriate to recall here briefly the new data presented by L. Cayeux in this reference concerning the age of formation of the cherts of the chalk. These data are predominantly derived from the Paris Basin, and particularly from the chalk cliffs of the Channel (region of Etretat).

1. *The formation of cherts, both as tabular masses and nodules, precedes the jointing and faulting of the chalk.*

This is the case of a fault west of Saint-Valéry-en-Caux with a vertical throw of about one meter (fig. 1, Cayeux's fig. 10). In the instances of maximum complication, a drag of the two portions of the chert bed toward the fault takes place through rupturing and not through deformation. It is followed by separation of the fragments which occur isolated in the fault plane. In the opposite situation, only throw and

Fig. 1. Tabular chert showing dislocation and drag by a fault (ff), west of Saint-Valéry-en-Caux (chalk with *M.c. anguinum*).

drag through fragmentation along the margins of the fault may be seen. In both cases the cherts are obviously older than the dislocations.

2. *The stringers and beds of cherts have recorded an erosional action contemporaneous with sedimentation, a situation which implies that the formation of the cherts preceded such an action.*

For instance, horizontal stringers of cherts are cut off by an inclined bed of cemented chalk, and vice-versa oblique stringers of cherts are truncated by a horizontal bed of cemented chalk (fig. 2, Cayeux's fig. 11). Also, oblique stringers of chert are interrupted by a horizontal tabular bed of chert. The maximum complication is reached by several cases of chert stringers displaying cross-bedding (fig. 3, Cayeux's fig. 12; fig. 4, Cayeux's fig. 13).

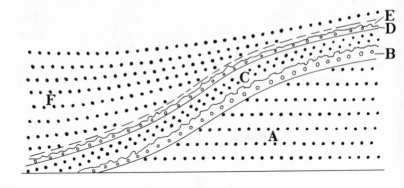

Fig. 2. Section of the chalk with cherts, west of Saint-Valéry-en-Caux.
   A. Hébert's chalk with zoned cherts showing horizontal string-
      ers of cherts truncated by an oblique bed of nodular chalk
      B.
   C. Chalk with chert nodules aligned in oblique stringers.
   D. Inclined bed of nodular chalk.
   E. Discontinuous tabular chert, also inclined.
   F. Hébert's chalk with weathered cherts (*silex cariés*) resting
      with an angular unconformity over zones E, D and C (chalk
      with *M.c. anguinum*).

Cherts, arranged as stringers, and rarely as continuous beds—associated or not with beds of nodular chalk—outline small, well-defined depressions, concentrically arranged, all of which are truncated by a horizontal bed of nodular chalk or of chert (fig. 5, Cayeux's fig. 14).

Finally, stringers of cherts form concentric depressions enclosed between two horizontal beds of nodular chalk which truncate them, above and below. In other words, the lower stringers overlie with an angular unconformity a bed of nodular chalk (fig. 6, Cayeux's fig. 15).

All these occurrences, and many others, result from a well characterized stratification due to current action and occurring in zones which themselves contain numerous evidences of ruptures of equilibrium such as beds of cemented chalk and submarine erosional surfaces. In conclusion, the cherts record perfectly all the disturbances of the sedimentation, as if their formation were affected by all the influences acting on the sea bottom.

These facts tend to prove that the cherts were forming, so to speak, at the same time as the chalk was being deposited, a necessary condition for their being affected by the processes of submarine erosion which involved the chalk itself many times.

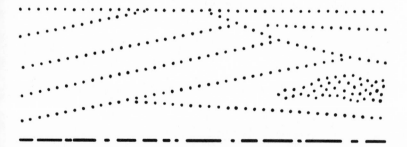

Fig. 3. Cross-bedded stringers of chert in the chalk with *M.c. anguinum* of Etretat.

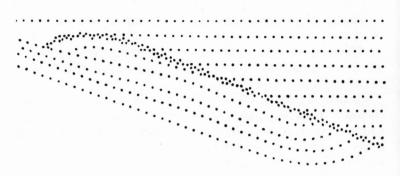

Fig. 4. Cross-bedded stringers of chert in the chalk with *M.c. anguinum* of Etretat.

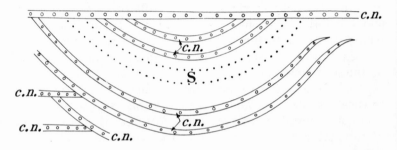

Fig. 5. Stringers of chert (S) and beds of nodular chalk (c.n.), arranged in concentric depressions and overlain unconformably by a horizontal bed of nodular chalk (c.n.). Cliffs east of Etretat (chalk with *M.c. anguinum*).

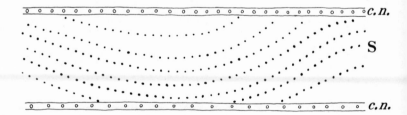

Fig. 6. Stringers of chert (S) arranged in concentric depressions lie unconformably over a horizontal bed of nodular chalk (c.n.), and are truncated at the top by another horizontal bed of nodular chalk (c.n.). Cliffs of Etretat (chalk with *M.c. anguinum*).

3. *Stringers of cherts participate in foldings of the chalk preceding its final emergence.*

This situation corresponds to a bed of chalk two meters thick which, by means of its stringers of cherts and an enclosed layer of cemented chalk, shows a sharp recumbent fold overlain and underlain by undisturbed horizontal chalks (fig. 7, Cayeux's fig. 16). This situation could only have been generated immediately after the deposition of the involved chalk, and it also implies a high enough degree of consistency of the chalk allowing the different beds to keep their individuality. [This situation could be interpreted as a submarine slumping].

4. *The tabular and nodular cherts were generated at such a time that they could be reworked within the chalk enclosing them.*

Chert beds frequently grade laterally into monogenetic breccias, demonstrating a submarine fragmentation process as well as an extreme fragility of the cherts which allows them

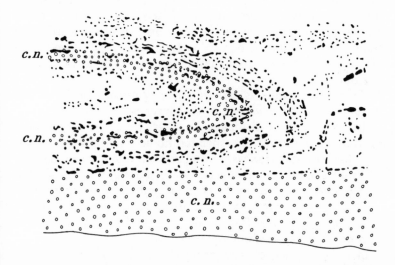

Fig. 7. Stringers of chert and bed of nodular chalk (c.n.) arranged in a kind of recumbent fold and underlain by a horizontal bed of nodular chalk (c.n.). The whole structure is overlain by a chalk with horizontal stringers of chert. Cliffs west of Etretat.

to be broken into angular debris and splinters without the intervention of a powerful dynamic action. In other words, the cherts had acquired their final degree of hardness and their present physical characteristics, when they were broken on the sea floor and their fragments transported and concentrated into sedimentary breccias.

Furthermore, the cherts were already provided with their present external patina when reworked within the chalk which was undergoing deposition. A given debris may show a rim of patina, whereas another, originating from the central part of a tabular or nodular chert, is devoid of it. This demonstrates that the patina is an original feature of cherts, a situation confirmed by the fact that recent fractures across cherts are never accompanied by any development of patina.

5. *The generation of the cherts of the magnesian chalks precedes dolomitization which is itself almost contemporaneous with sedimentation.*

It is possible to prove in several instances, that the formation of the cherts of the magnesian chalk has taken place between the deposition of the chalk and its dolomitization and erosion on the sea floor. In other words, the generation of the cherts has followed very closely the deposition of the components of the chalky mud on the sea bottom.

6. *In a given chalk, chert veins were formed exactly at the same time as nodular and tabular types.*

This situation is displayed by chert veins whose patina is continuous with that of associated nodular and tabular types. In a few other instances, the cherts in veins are of slightly different age and the respective patinas remain independent.

7. *The occurrence of chert veins only at certain levels in the chalk cliffs, and the textural differentiation of the cherts within successive layers, strongly indicate a formation preceding the final emergence of the chalk.*

In general, each chert-bearing chalk has a peculiar aspect precisely due to its cherts and so characteristic that cherts may replace fossils for a trained geologist mapping a chalky terrane. This situation shows that the features of the cherts are original and generated at the time of deposition of their enclosing chalk, under a variety of environmental conditions, and not at all after the final emergence of the entire sequence of superposed chalks. In summary, when the deposition of a given chalk was completed, the history of its siliceous accidents was also finished.

22. L. CAYEUX, *op. cit.*, p. 593.

23. L. CAYEUX, Nouvelles données sur l'âge relatif des silex: *C.R. Somm. Soc. Géol. France*, 1935, No. 12, pp. 173-175.

The phosphatic formation of Rebiba, in central Tunisia, provides very precise data concerning the time of formation of its cherts, and simultaneously allows a very sophisticated study of their history. The formation contains two phosphatic beds, separated by a limestone reaching a maximum thickness of 1.20 m, but locally absent by erosion. This intermediate limestone contains light yellow-tan cherts, devoid of patina. These cherts are so unique within the entire phosphatic group of Rebiba that they can be very easily identified whenever reworked to a variable extent. Some of them are remarkably regular in shape and subspherical, others variably flattened and mammillated. Large perforations, appearing as irregularly-shaped phosphatic boudins, start from the base of the upper layer and extend deeply within the underlying chert-bearing limestone.

In this instance the determination of the relative age of the cherts is ideally simple:

1. Nodules belonging to the limestone, from which they have been removed by reworking processes following erosion, are scattered on the very surface of the limestone. These nodules, flattened and very mammillated, are perforated on all sides by tiny tubules reaching at the most 2 mm in diameter. Therefore, these cherts existed before the reworking took place.

2. Some cherts, generated at the top of the intermediate limestone in which they remain enclosed, are related to the previously mentioned large phosphatic perforations. For instance, one of these cherts has incorporated a phosphatic

boudin, demonstrating that its formation followed that of the large perforations. Unfortunately, this observation does not provide any age limit.

3. Some cherts, loosened by erosion at the upper part of the limestone to which they are still attached by their basis, display beautiful examples of compound nodules. These consist of two parts formed during two very distinct phases.

In a given sample, one can observe the first phase chert, free over most of its external surface, and the second phase reduced to an incipient envelope. The latter encloses a phosphatic boudin which does not penetrate at all into the first phase chert.

A very large compound nodule shows a strongly mammillated chert, partially enclosed within a second phase chert. The latter contains several large phosphatic boudins which twist around the chert of the first phase without penetrating into it.

Consequently, the first phase precedes the generation of the large phosphatic perforations, and the second clearly follows it. In other words, the large perforations were generated in the intermediate limestone between the first and the second phase of formation of the cherts.

The cherts belonging to the preceding category are also characterized by numerous minute perforations which affect only the second phase. This restricted distribution remains completely unexplained in the present state of our knowledge.

A more accurate time determination may be obtained from the occurrence at the base of the upper phosphatic bed of rounded pebbles of chert, derived from the intermediate limestone, and replete with minute perforations equally distributed over their entire surface. Therefore, a very precise age limit can be assigned to all the cherts of the limestone.

Conclusions

Three major conclusions may be reached from this brief investigation:

1. Cherts were formed during the deposition of their parent-rock. Such is the case of the nodules reworked at the

surface of the limestone, and of the nodules belonging to the first phase of the compound cherts.

2. Among the numerous cherts generated in a single phase, some were formed before the reworking of the limestone, such are the reworked and perforated cherts observed at the very surface of the limestone; the others were generated later when the limestone had already undergone large phosphatic perforations. Therefore, the generation of certain simple cherts and the formation of the second phase of the compound cherts are contemporaneous.

3. In all cases, the development of the simple and compound cherts was terminated at the time of deposition of the stringer of chert pebbles located at the base of the upper phosphatic bed.

Neither the new data on the rapid and submarine generation of the cherts, nor those previously collected on the same subject (L. Cayeux, Les roches sédimentaires de France. Roches siliceuses: *Mém. Carte Géol. France*, 1929, pp. 588-594. See also footnote 21), allow to state that all the cherts of the limestones were generated under the same conditions. In spite of a few exceptions, the rule, nevertheless, seems to have a character of broad generality.

24. It seems superfluous to warn the reader that the above lines do not pretend to abstract the entire and very complex history of the cherts. In this volume only one of its episodes is of interest to us.

25. L. CAYEUX, Les minerais de fer oolithique de France. II. Minerais de fer secondaires: *Etudes Gîtes Min. France, Min. Trav. Publics*, 1922, pp. 423-426.

Cayeux assumes the following mechanism for the generation of the calcareous nodules of the oolitic iron ores of Lorraine.

Actually the ores, always heterogeneous, consist of an association of calcareous and oolitic concentrations generated by a mechanical sorting of the constituents. The first correspond to the portions with the highest amount of organic debris, mainly Molluscan remains. Obviously, the formation of the nodules is initiated by these concentrations of very fragmented shells. They play the role of centers of attraction of the calcium carbonate which cemented the constituents at the time of consolidation of the deposits. This process is similar to that of the generation of cherts. In both cases, organisms, either siliceous or calcareous, attract toward them a circulating solution of same chemical composition and determine the formation of siliceous or calcareous concretions. Actually, calcareous nodules never develop in portions where ferruginous oolites are abundant, and the occurrence of numerous calcareous organic debris is the condition *sine qua non* for the morphological differentiation of the calcium carbonate.

26. L. CAYEUX, *op. cit.*, pp. 444-445. (fig. 8, Cayeux's fig. 23)

27. L. CAYEUX, Les "boulets calcaires" de la formation phosphatée du Bassin de Gafsa (Tunisie) et les enseignements qui découlent de leur étude: *C.R. Acad. Sc. Paris*, 1939, vol. 208, pp. 1951-1953. See footnote 15.

28. I have presented a comprehensive study of this structure in which all its known varieties are discussed. (L. Cayeux, *Les roches sédimentaires de France. Roches*

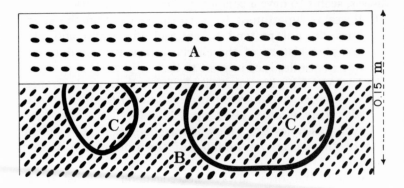

Fig. 8. Calcareous nodules of the gray bed of Valleroy with their upper parts truncated.
    A. Limestone with ferruginous oolites.
    B. Very calcareous ore with obliquely stratified oolites.
    C. Truncated nodules.

carbonatées *(Calcaires et Dolomies)*; 1935, Paris, Masson et Cie, pp. 182-206.

See also annotated and updated translation by A. V. Carozzi, 1970, Darien, Conn., Hafner Publishing Company, pp. 168-190.

29. Ed. HEBERT, Note sur la craie blanche et la craie marneuse dans le Bassin de Paris, et sur la division de ce dernier étage en quatre assises: *Bull. Soc. Géol. France*, 1863, Ser. 2, vol. XX, pp. 605-631.

    Ibid., Ondulations de la craie dans le Bassin de Paris: *Bull. Soc. Géol. France*, 1872, Ser. 2, vol. XXIX, pp. 446-472 and pp. 583-594.

30. W. WHITAKER, The geology of the London Basin. The Chalk and the Eocene beds of the southern and western tracts: *Mem. Geol. Survey of England and Wales*, 1872, vol. IV, p. 46.

    Ibid., *The geology of London and of part of the Thames Valley*: 1889, Geological Survey of England and Wales, Topographical Memoirs, 2 vols., Chap. 29, Petrological, Mineralogical and Chemical. The minute structure of the chalk by W. Hill, pp. 517-523.

31. Ch. BARROIS, Recherches sur le terrain crétacé supérieur de l'Angleterre et de l'Irlande: *Mém. Soc. Géol. Nord*, 1876, vol. I, pp. 174-175.

32. L. CAYEUX, Les roches sédimentaires de France. Roches siliceuses: *Mém. Carte géol. France*, 1929, p. 586, fig. 14. See footnote 21.

33. J. MURRAY and A.F. RENARD, Deep Sea Deposits in *Rep. of the scient. results of the exploring voyage of H.M.S. Challenger during the years 1873-1876*: 1891, p. 50.

34. *Ibid.*, *id.*, p. 96.

35. *Ibid.*, *id.*, p. 98.

36. According to J. Murray and A.F. Renard, (*op. cit.* p. 171) these nodules could be hardened portions of a deep-sea deposit formed at a much greater depth, and subsequently elevated into their present position, prob-

ably by the same movements which uplifted the neighboring islands.

37. L. CAYEUX, Contribution à l'étude micrographique des
terrains sédimentaires: *Mém. Soc. Géol. Nord*, 1897, vol.
IV, 2, pp. 553-557.

As early as 1872, Ed. Hébert described beds of cemented
chalk with nodular upper surfaces, often perforated, within
the normal chalk. He interpreted them as proofs of inter-
ruptions of sedimentation, of oscillatory movements of
uplifting, of reworking by shallow waters, and even of
emergence of the sea floor. In other words, these marker beds
represented for Hébert the expression of shoreline
conditions.

On the basis of the observations of the "Challenger" and
of the "Blake", I feel that the processes of cementation and
of generation of the nodular structure which accidentally
affect the chalk of the Paris Basin, may occur in present-day
sediments and on the sea-floor itself. They are mostly the
result of an interruption of sedimentation due to the action
of currents, and do not require necessarily an emergence.

In my opinion, the beds of cemented and perforated chalk
correspond to the hard grounds reported by the "Challenger". In spite of insufficient petrographic work, these beds
have revealed that the mineral constituents do not seem to
have been affected by the unusual conditions which generated them; only the Foraminifers display a high degree of
fragmentation. The proof of an interruption of sedimentation
is in particular given by the occurrence of oysters covered by
a phosphatic coating and attached to the upper surface of the
cemented beds with *M.c. anguinum* at the contact with the
phosphatic chalk.

However, certain types of local cementation of the chalk
and some occurrences of the nodular structure were unquestionably generated after the emergence of the chalk. Therefore, recent processes cannot explain the complete range of
these features which are polygenetic in origin.

In summary, within the emerged deposits and under
conditions different from those active on the sea floor,

transformations may occur which are identical to those which took place during sedimentation. This is one of the most remarkable phenomena displayed by sedimentary rocks which greatly complicates their investigation; each occurrence requiring a particular examination.

However, many observations show that dynamic processes should be considered as an important factor during all stages of the depositional history of the chalk. They transported minerals and organisms, fragmented the tests and skeletons of invertebrates, and finally deeply modified the aspect and texture of the chalk.

38. L. CAYEUX, Les minerais de fer oolithique de France. II. Minerais de fer secondaires: *Etudes Gîtes Min. France, Min. Trav. Publics,* 1922, pp. 939-945.

General metamorphism among oolitic iron ores

Under the designation of general metamorphism, I include all the physical and chemical modifications undergone by the ferruginous formations since their deposition and under the exclusive influence of external agents. Some of them are *mineral neoformations* and others, changes of physical nature, mainly *cementation phenomena.*

Mineral neoformations.

In the oolitic iron ores, the amount of chemical and mineralogical changes attributed to the general metamorphism is very high and has no equivalent among any other known sedimentary formation. In order to appreciate its importance, the initial condition of the oolitic iron ores should be recalled: calcareous materials, such as oolites and organisms in the presence of marine waters containing iron in solution; these are the essential original components of the ores. All the following constituents are derived from them: siderite, chlorites, brown and red hematite (both amorphous and crystalline), specular hematite, magnetite, pyrite, glauconite; several varieties of silica, such as quartz in grains, crystals and spherulites; chalcedony and opal; the calcite of the cement; calcium phosphate in concretions; iron phosphate; manganese oxide; orthoclase, without mentioning the compounds of magnesium, of phosphorus and of iron invisible under the microscope. Therefore, a total of about twenty distinct mineral species are to be attributed to the general metamorphism.

Most of these constituents can be formed in the generating environment as well as within the deposited ore. Among them are all the ferruginous compounds, with perhaps the exception of glauconite, too rare to afford a demonstration of the duality of origin.

The quartz, very abundant as a secondary mineral in the ores of Lorraine, was formed almost entirely in the generating environment, and in a very small amount *in situ*. The orthoclase also belongs to the generating environment whenever it is an integrant part of fragments of reworked ores. Perhaps all of the orthoclase has such an origin. I shall come back later to this question.

Cementation phenomena

The analysis of the iron ores has provided the greatest number of new data on this subject because of the innumerable debris of reworked ores occurring in all the investigated rocks. Through them, we have learned that cementation occurs simultaneously with the formation of the ores. This is so true that reworked fragments occur, within a given bed, from bottom to top. Consequently, such a layer, in its initial phase of deposition, was already receiving fragments having undergone complete mineralogical evolution and cementation, although originating from the destroyed extension of that same bed. There are even instances of materials having undergone a double reworking and a double cementation before final deposition.

In spite of the puzzling rapidity of the processes which follow each other and lead to the formation of the first reworked fragments of an ore, we are compelled to accept such clear and obvious facts. Truly, *the entire history of the Mesozoic oolitic iron ores is dominated by the occurrence of fragments of reworked ores and by its consequences.*

Perhaps it is not superfluous to insist on the fact that we are not dealing with a partial cementation, sufficient to keep the constituents together during their transportation, but with a completed cementation. Mechanical actions reached such a high degree of intensity in the environment where the constituents of the ore were in motion, that oolites were broken and organisms reduced to minute debris, and often shaped into small pebbles or pseudoolites. Therefore, the fragments could not have kept their individuality unless their constituents were solidly bound together. The degree of cementation must have been carried really very far because, for instance, pseudoolites and organic debris enclosed in a fragment of reworked ore, have been truncated along its margins either by abrasion or by impact without dissociation of any of the constituents. Finally, the very angular shape of some fragments demonstrates that they had acquired the hardness of a cemented rock before their reworking. If needed, the lack of any trace of volume change would lead toward the same interpretation.

What I have just said concerning the rapidity of cementation phenomena applies not only to the ferruginous components but to the calcium carbonate as well. Indeed, reworked materials demonstrate that they were completely solid at the time of their reworking. I have also observed for the calcium carbonate instances of double reworking implying a double rapid cementation as in the case of the ferruginous elements. The best argument in favor of a large-scale development of calcite, following immediately the generation of the ore, is afforded by the calcareous concentrations (nodules) of the ores of Lorraine whose formation preceded the complete deposition of the layer containing them. No matter how strongly one would like to escape such conclusions, apparently in complete opposition to presently accepted ideas, one is compelled to generalize the concept formulated for the ores of Lorraine. Therefore, I shall state the following conclusion: *Whenever the deposition of a layer of oolitic iron ore is completed, its history is so to speak also finished.* Indeed, the subsequent modifications generated by atmospheric agents are of very little importance when compared to the sum of the changes which took place during deposition.

In other words, in this particular case, the time factor does not at all have the importance usually attributed to it, and consequently the essential features of an oolitic iron ore must be independent of its age.

Concept of a general submarine metamorphism

The idea of a submarine metamorphism came to my mind during numerous fieldtrips of applied geology in Normandy, and after the examination of the cores of drillings, undertaken upon my advice, for exploring the subsurface extension of the Basin of May.

The features discussed above, show that *the history of our oolitic iron ores has taken place under the sea.* Besides, numerous iron ores have been reworked without any associated emergence. Therefore, *this general metamorphism is, at least in most of the cases, a submarine process.* This is the conclusion that should be reached if one relies only on demonstrated facts. In my mind, I am tempted to consider no exception in the case of oolitic iron ores.

At any rate, some of the above-mentioned neoformations are of particular interest in relation to the environment which generated them. For instance, the secondary quartz of the ores of Lorraine, in all its aspects, represents a large amount of silica, and is a submarine product. The same is true for the orthoclase of the fragments of reworked ores.

This conclusion applies to all the ferruginous compounds of our ores, and particularly to magnetite, commonly attributed to special metamorphic actions, and even to igneous influences.

In summary, in the domain of the oolitic iron ores—the only one to be considered here—submarine metamorphism is a general process extremely varied in its effects.

At this point, it appears legitimate to ask to what extent these processes belong to past geologic times. We have been reasoning since a long time under the influence of the doctrine of present causes, although the present is obviously not a continuation of the past in all the fields of geology. It is sufficient to recall what I have said about the environment proper to the generation of the oolitic iron ores, to immediately realize that the conditions which have prevailed at the different times of formation of these ores, have no equivalent in present seas. The large-scale ruptures of equilibrium which have played a fundamental role in the generation of the iron ores, are unknown today. Their absence seems to imply that of the generating environments of ferruginous oolites, not a single example is displayed today. [This statement is no longer correct. For a discussion of Recent marine ferruginous oolites, see Editor's Introduction.] On this subject as well as on many others, the doctrine of present causes is in default.

Therefore, should we reach the conclusion that the general submarine metamorphism is a phenomenon peculiar to iron ores only, with no equivalent outside their domain? I do not think so. My observations on a few deposits, besides ores, tend to prove that the process also affected other types of formations. However, it is not known if present submarine bottoms escape its influence or not.

Here is the little we know on this subject. In several places in the oceans, the soundings of the *Challenger* have encountered hard grounds devoid of any sediment in the process of being deposited. Elsewhere, other kinds of cemented bottoms have been found consisting of shells and fragments of volcanic rocks. In all instances, no sedimentation was taking place. These unusual places range in depth between 510 and 6,600 feet. Some of them, such as those reported off Spain (1,950 to 4,350 feet depth) are located in the zone of terrigenous sediments where deposition is active.

Furthermore, the cruise of the *Blake* has demonstrated the occurrence of cemented limestones along the path of warm currents. For instance, on the Pourtalès Plateau, offshore Florida, cemented limestone is being formed at a depth of 160 meters down to 500-600 meters. Therefore, the sea floor may accidentally consist of hard rocks.

What is then the precise significance of the hard grounds found by the *Challenger*? Do they represent bottoms under the influence of currents responsible for the cementation of the sediments which elsewhere remain unconsolidated? If such were the case, the present submarine metamorphism would be extremely localized and devoid of any general significance. Is the generation of hard grounds only that, or perhaps on the contrary, the expression of a rather general phenomenon, which is only accidentally revealed to us? Since a long time, I have been more inclined toward the second alternative. Instead of assuming that currents cement certain parts of the sea-bottom, I think that they simply have an erosional action, which locally reveals cemented sediments hidden everywhere else under the cover of the muds and oozes, presently being deposited. In other words, what has been considered as an exception would be the rule, and the submarine metamorphism would have its place among present general processes. If such were the case, the field of application of the doctrine of present causes would be greatly enlarged.

However, far from my mind is the thought that the general metamorphism is everywhere and always a submarine process and that, in present nature, the freshly deposited sediments are all undergoing cementation! The great number of ancient formations which have remained unconsolidated indicates that at all times, or almost, some sediments have escaped its action. Besides, I am keeping in mind the fact that dynamometamorphism and atmospheric agents still play their role in the transformation of soft sediments into cemented rocks. The respective parts of all these processes in the general economy of the world will be difficult to establish for a long time to come.

Regardless of one's opinion about this problem, it is obvious that each progress in the knowledge of ancient seas reveals our great ignorance of what is happening on the floor of present oceans. May I state that, in a geological viewpoint, Oceanography has betrayed the hopes that the exploration of the *Challenger* had allowed to build on it? After having gained some knowledge of the nature and distribution of present sediments, we seem less interested in the modern deposits than in the ancient ones. By combining the results of the analysis of the ancient sediments with our scanty knowledge of recent deposits, it is reasonable to assume that already at a very shallow depth beneath the sea floor, the sediments undergo physical and chemical modifications which may be interpreted as an incipient general metamorphism. We have only a very vague idea on the possible output of such a laboratory in which the sea water, pressure and often organic matter are the most important agents. The future will certainly show that its role has been largely unrecognized, and that by giving a great importance to meteoric waters in the general metamorphism, we have considerably exaggerated their influence at the expense of the submarine metamorphism.

39. L. CAYEUX, The phosphatic nodules of the Agulhas Bank (A study of submarine geology): *Annals South African Museum*, 1934, vol. XXXI, pp. 128-135.

See footnote 16.

L. CAYEUX, Les ressources minérales de la France d'Outre-Mer. IV. Le Phosphate: *Publ. bureau d'études géologiques et minières coloniales*, 1935, Paris, Soc. Edit. Géogr. Marit. et Coloniales. Les phosphates de chaux sédimentaires. Manières d'être et mode de formation, pp. 8-11.

This reference is an abstract in French of Cayeux's publication on the phosphatic nodules of the Agulhas Bank.

40. L. CAYEUX, Les phosphates de chaux sédimentaires de France: *Etudes Gîtes Min. France, Serv. de la Carte Géol. France et des Tops. Sout.*, 1939, vol. I, pp. 79-83.

The Carboniferous black phosphates of the Pyrenees and of the Montagne-Noire display a certain number of common features which make them appear as very closely related. These features are: *occurrence of very numerous Radiolarians to the exclusion of other organisms; complete absence of detrital minerals; abundance of carbonaceous matter; frequent concretionary structure of the calcium phosphate, and intimate association of both types of black phosphates with black radiolarites (LYDIENNES), themselves variably phosphatic.*

Regardless of their provenance, these phosphates derive from deposits which originally contained a great number of Radiolarians, and therefore they occupy an unusual position within the immense group of sedimentary phosphorites. Furthermore, *they represent ancient Radiolarian oozes sensu stricto, whose degree of purity is equal to, if not greater than that of similar present oozes*, except for the presence of calcium phosphate and carbonaceous matter. In the samples where the Radiolarians have least suffered from the far-reaching modifications undergone by the sediment, after deposition of the materials on the sea floor, one recognizes either only Radiolarians (Pyrenees), or Radiolarians associated with numerous debris forming a groundmass comparable to the "fine-washings" of the Radiolarian oozes dredged by the *Challenger* (Montagne-Noire).

In order to reach their present facies, the parent-rocks must have been deeply modified. In essence, the calcium phosphate underwent a differentiation characterized by a variably globular and crystalline state, and the carbonaceous material a change in nature which makes it a product most probably colloidal at the origin and susceptible of great mobility. Consequently, these phosphates represent a very aberrant and unique group among the large spectrum of sedimentary phosphorites. . .

The organisms themselves have been affected by the deep changes undergone by the parent-rocks. Radiolarians were at least quartzified, and in most of the cases replaced by calcium phosphate and carbonaceous matter. In the exceptional occurrences of Sponge spicules, the latter were quartzified and phosphatized.

Chemically, these phosphates belong to the category of medium-rich varieties with a content of phosphoric acid of about 30%. Only the nodules from the Pyrenees remained calcareous.

Although the complete history of the nodules is not understood, a few aspects of it are clear. Obviously, they represent portions of Radiolarian oozes, consolidated in the original shape of nodules, generally flattened or subspherical, but never angular. Most probably, their generation is slightly later than sedimentation and they were never scattered over the sea floor as the nodules dredged from present oceans. This situation seems confirmed by the fact that not a single nodule carries any incrustation of organic origin, in other words, they remained buried within the deposit which generated them. However, this is not an absolute criterion, because in other instances nodules which are obviously reworked can be devoid of incrustations. . .

The morphology of the nodules is that of concretions and does not, as generally assumed, result from dynamic actions. Their weight, reaching 20 to 30 kilograms, excludes any transportation into areas of the sea floor where sediments do not display any trace of the slightest agitation. The role of mechanical agents was extremely reduced in the shaping of these concretions, as shown by the petrographic examination of numerous nodules in which Radiolarians, although of extremely delicate structure, do not present the least deformation.

Therefore, we visualize the original deposit corresponding to the present phosphatic formation as a mud, very siliceous through its Radiolarians, unusually rich in organic matter and somewhat phosphatic and calcareous. This mud has undergone three far-reaching transformations, resulting from the migration of the silica of numerous Radiolarians, the redistribution of the carbonaceous matter in a new form, and the concentration and fixation of the calcium phosphate as nodules.

Concerning the origin of the calcium phosphate, I would like to point out the complete absence of fragments of bony tissue throughout the investigated sequence. The abundance of microorganisms mentioned above naturally implies an excess of organic matter, and consequently a certain amount of phosphoric acid accumulated on the sea bottom. However, such a source, without disregarding its importance, does not seem adequate to account for the tonnage represented by the phosphate deposits.

The similarity which I have drawn between the phosphatic formation and the Radiolarian oozes naturally raises a petrographic objection due to the occurrence of calcium phosphate and a high proportion of carbonaceous matters, substances which have no equivalent in present Radiolarian oozes.

Actually, the large-scale occurrence of organic matters does not represent such an unsurmountable difficulty. Let us recall that large amounts of floated wood, transported during the floods of the Mississippi, are deposited eventually in the Gulf of Mexico, far offshore and at great depths, over portions of the sea floor covered with a *Globigerina* ooze. Such a situation does not prevent the deposit from preserving the typical features of a *Globigerina* ooze. This is also true of the phosphatic formation which, although displaying the essential characteristics of a Radiolarian ooze, differs from it by the abundant inclusions of organic matters.

Similarly, the occurrence of calcium phosphate does not contradict the proposed similarity. *After due consideration, one is led to ask if the sequence of present sediments is not conducive to errors, when we undertake comparisons, because it represents an epoch of great stability of the sea floor.* There is such a close relationship between the great ruptures of equilibrium undergone by the sea floor and the large-scale generation of sedimentary phosphorites, that it is precisely because such conditions are not realized today that the generation of large phosphatic deposits does not occur at present. In that respect, *the series of present deposits is somewhat aberrant*, and I feel that one cannot use the occurrence of calcium phosphate in the Radiolarian muds of the Pyrenees and the Montagne-Noire as an argument against their interpretation as typical Radiolarian oozes. *In this case, as well as in many others, the doctrine of present causes is in default.*

The most difficult aspect of this subject is to reach a rational concept of the generating environment of the phosphates with Radiolarians, a problem which pertains directly to the habitat of these organisms. In our opinion, it is clearly demonstrated that both deposits derive from a typically pelagic sediment, generated outside any continental influence, except for the carbonaceous material. This situation does not necessarily imply a considerable distance from the shoreline. The idea of extreme quietness expressed by the perfect preservation of delicate Radiolarians and the arrangement of the materials forming the enclosing shales, can explain the complete absence of minerals derived from the continent, considering a certain distance from the shoreline—an assumption which is not unreasonable.

The bathymetrical question is more difficult to solve. I may recall that the analysis of the black radiolarites (*lydiennes*), intimately associated with the black phosphates of the Pyrenees, has led me to consider that abyssal forms were absent, a conclusion which naturally applies also to the calcium phosphates (L. Cayeux, Les roches sédimentaires de France. Roches siliceuses: *Mém. Carte Géol. France*, 1929, p. 336). The so-called benthonic types which occur in the phosphates are too poorly preserved to be of any use. Relying essentially on the exclusive occurrence of Radiolarians and the absence of minerals derived from the coast, I continue to assume that the black radiolarites were deposited in deep water, although I cannot express this concept with figures. Logically, the same interpretation should apply to the phosphates which cannot be dissociated from the black radiolarites. A similar conclusion has been reached by Zb. Sujkowski in his study of the black radiolarites and phosphates of the Dinantian of Poland (Zb. Sujkowski, Radiolarites du Carbonifère inférieur du Massif de Sainte-Croix: *Bull. Serv. géol. Pologne*, 1933, vol. VII, p. 705).

The very rare megascopic fossils found in the phosphatic formation, mainly phyllocarid Crustaceans and Cirripedia, do not provide additional data for any bathymetrical interpretation.

From all the above-mentioned facts we can visualize a large basin undergoing a peculiar type of sedimentation starting with the lower Viséan. By its fauna of siliceous Rhizopoda, this basin formed a well individualized zoological province. Its domain, whose eastern and western limits are unknown, was centered in the Pyrenees, and stretched to the Montagne-Noire and to Catalonia. Over this entire area, Radiolarian oozes were deposited, to be converted into black radiolarites and phosphatic nodules. This basin was only a portion of the sea with Radiolarians of that particular time, as demonstrated by the absence of all constituents derived from emerged land, except vegetable debris. Actually, this sea extended far beyond the above-mentioned domain; eastward it reached Upper Silesia through the Harz and Thuringia, westward it may be followed into Asturia.

All these data should now be combined with the fundamental fact that the phosphatic formation is separated from its Devonian substratum by a great hiatus, which in some cases involves the terminal part of the Famennian, and is devoid of traces of erosion and of any basal conglomerate. Since an emergence appears unlikely, this hiatus could be due to a phase of submarine erosion which would have destroyed all the missing deposits. However, the extent of the area involved and the thickness of the sediments supposedly eliminated, represent serious objections to this interpretation.

In spite of the size of the affected domain and of the duration of the phenomenon, I would be tempted to attribute the hiatus to a long interruption of sedimentation. This hypothesis, even with its shortcomings, would explain the gap as well as the pelagic character of the first Viséan sediments. Regardless of the final answer, it is certain that the renewed sedimentation which generated the phosphates has been preceded by a far-reaching disturbance involving an immense area and which belongs to the complex group of the ruptures of equilibrium, generators of calcium phosphate.

41. Al. AGASSIZ, *A contribution to American Thalassography. Three cruises of the United States Coast and Geodetic Survey steamer "Blake" in the Gulf of Mexico, in the Caribbean Sea and along the Atlantic Coast of the United States from 1877 to 1880*: 1888, Boston and New York, Houghton, Mifflin, vol. I, p. 276, fig. 189.

42. L. CAYEUX, *Les roches sédimentaires de France. Roches carbonatées (Calcaires et Dolomies)*, 1935, Paris, Masson, pp. 348-351, fig. 7. See also updated English translation by A.V. Carozzi, 1970, Darien, Conn., Hafner Publishing Company, pp. 323-326, fig. 7.

Yellow chalks of the region of Etretat (Seine-Inférieure).

The cliff to the east of the harbor of Etretat (upstream cliff) shows a lens of chalk, belonging probably to the upper part of the Turonian, with deeply modified physical characters (fig. 9, Cayeux's fig. 7). This lenticular body, less than 100 meters long and at the most 2 meters thick, is deeply channeled by a conglomeratic chalk. It comes down to the level of the beach, and the following section may be observed for a length of about 30 meters.

1. The lower chalk of the lenticular body (C) is coarse-grained, granular, replete with cavities visible with a hand lens, and, like the chalks with callosities, displays numerous specks of manganese oxide. Under the microscope, the rock appears very closely related to the normal chalk, particularly because of its high content of organisms. No detrital mineral is visible. Cavities are present everywhere, reaching several hundreds in a given thin section. Some of them display a

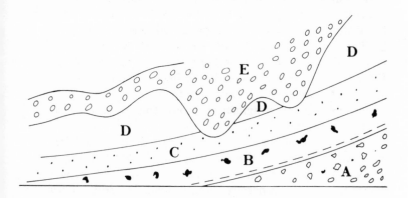

Fig. 9. Relationships between the yellow chalk of Etretat and the surrounding formations.

    A. Conglomeratic chalk, with or without cherts.

    B. Gray chalk containing very irregular nodules as well as discontinuous layers of ferruginous cherts (1.50 m).

    C. Yellowish hard chalk grading laterally into white chalk, and into the underlying chalk (B).

    D. Yellow and crystalline chalk, increasingly indurated upwards, and abruptly interrupted by layer E (C + D = 2 m).

    E. Very conglomeratic chalk, deeply channelling the lenticular body of indurated chalk, leading to the disappearance at two places of the entire bed D and of a portion of bed C.

perfect rhombohedral shape, while others correspond to associations of grains limited geometrically along their free side; and many others, without being very irregular, do not have a morphology that implies the idea of a dissolved carbonate. In this particular example, the sizes of the dissolved rhombohedra are much larger than those of the crystals observed in the above-described yellow chalks.

Actually, this rock displays the greatest analogies with the yellow chalks which cement the callosities, and, unquestionably, the destruction of the elements corresponding today to the cavities, is related to an episode which is the same for the entire analyzed sequence. Except for the color, the rock is similar to the marble-like chalk of the vicinity of Vernon, in which the destruction of the rhombohedra is a generalized occurrence.

In spite of the complete elimination of the carbonate of the rhombohedra and of the grains, the rock contains .55% magnesium. Therefore, it is the remaining portion of the deposit, in other words, the non-modified chalk, which has fixed that substance, independently of the crystals.

2. The variety which builds the top of the lenticular body (D) recalls to such an extent the so-called magnesian chalk of Bimont, by its color, crystalline aspect and hardness, that any sample mixed with a collection from the quarry of Bimont could not be distinguished from the others without a microscopic study.

The rock consists almost entirely of rhombohedra, of a size comparable to the cavities of the underlying yellow chalk. All the crystals display at least two intersecting cleavage planes, generally emphasized by iron oxide and forming continuous lines or streaks of dots. All the crystals are also characterized by growth lines similarly emphasized by iron oxide, which forms continuous lines or streaks of dots separated by a variable interval. The final result is a very widespread, zoned structure. The occurrence of important concentrations of iron oxide and of ferruginous rhombohedral cores within the rhombohedra, should also be stressed. The latter, which are different from the above-described types by their sizes, cleavages and ferruginous inclusions, are nevertheless optically identical because each element is still an aggregate, rhombohedral or not.

The crystals are so numerous as to be in contact through their crystallographic faces, leaving only an insignificant space to the matrix. There are even areas in which the crystals are solidly juxtaposed. The small amount of carbonate which cements the crystals belongs to a colorless variety.

No other example chosen among the yellow chalks and the magnesian chalks, affords so many data in favor of the concept of the iron oxide being contemporaneous with the generation of the crystals. The study of the deposit itself leads to a similar conclusion. In that respect, the abrupt disappearance of the brown color at the top of the lens recalls what happens in the upper part of the magnesian chalk of Bimont.

The chemical composition of this rock is as follows:

SiO_2 (total)	1.05%	
SiO_2 (soluble)	—	.50
Al_2O_3	.20	
Fe_2O_3	1.35	
CaO	53.15	
MgO	1.24	
K_2O	.10	
Na_2O	.40	
P_2O_5	.10	
CO_2	42.51	
H_2O	—	
Total	100.10%	

The exact location of the magnesium, corresponding to 2.593% of the carbonate, is difficult to establish. Because of the extremely small role played by the matrix, a test with formic acid cannot be pinpointed, and therefore the results are unclear. At any rate, not a single element can be considered as dolomite, and we must assume that the calcium carbonate is somewhat magnesian.

The two chalks of the lenticular body of Etretat correspond to two distinct stages, usually associated in the chalk
with callosities, one characterized by a large scale generation
of composite rhombohedra; the other by the complete
solution of these same rhombohedra, as in the chalk of
Vernon. In the case described here, a very small increase in
magnesium content accompanied the transformation of the
chalk.

*Yellow chalks with MICRASTER BREVIPORUS of the Escaut valley
(Nord)*

The chalk with *M. breviporus* displays, in the Escaut
valley, the facies of hard and yellow chalk, which recalls the
yellow chalks of average hardness of Bimont and Etretat. It
achieves a great development from, and including, the region
of Catelet in the South, to Crèvecoeur in the North, and is
quarried as building stone in many places, particularly at
Vendhuile and Honnecourt. It occurs with the same features
at Moislains, north of Péronne (Somme).

This chalk, while containing abundant organisms, shows
the same changes as the chalk with typical callosities, but
with a minimum of development. Nevertheless, the cavities
left by the composite grains and crystals of calcite may
represent sometimes one third of the deposit. The areas
where these elements have been preserved may play a greatly
variable role from one sample to another.

The analysis of a yellow chalk from Honnecourt is as
follows:

SiO_2 (total)	2.25%
Al_2O_3	.30
Fe_2O_3	1.27
CaO	52.93
MgO	.65
K_2O	.20
Na_2O	.30
P_2O_5	.28
CO_2	41.70
H_2O	.55
Total:	100.43%

A chalk from Vendhuile had a magnesium content of .55%, and a sample from Moislains .40%.

As a whole, the above analysis corresponds to that of a normal and relatively very pure Turonian chalk, a condition not expressed by the lithologic characters of the rock.

Phosphatic yellow chalks

The processes which have generated composite rhombohedra and grains have been active in two very different environments. For instance, the same products, or the corresponding cavities, occur in low-content phosphatic chalks at the base of the zone with *B. quadrata* of Curlu, Méricourt, etc. (Somme). Megascopically, these chalks may be distinguished from the associated ones by their particular yellowish color, and their much greater coherence.

Abstract.

The indurated yellow or gray chalks, with or without callosities, are essentially characterized by the generation of numerous composite rhombohedra of calcite. Exceptionally, these rhombohedra are entirely preserved or dissolved; in general, they have undergone a partial destruction which has left residues appearing as hard nuclei called *durillons* (callosities). These modifications of purely physical nature are almost never accompanied by appreciable changes in magnesium content.

43. *Ibid., id.,* pp. 335 and 434.

Since the generation of dolomitic zones in the recently uplifted coral islands seems to be related to the tendency toward emergence of the reefs, we are logically led to wonder if the change of the white chalk with *M.c. anguinum*, into a magnesian chalk, could not be a consequence of the change of environment, following the uplifting of the sea-bottom which preceded the Campanian transgression.

44. *Ibid., id.,* p. 349. See footnote 42.

45. *Ibid., id.,* pp. 343-344.

In the Oise, at Bimont, near Breteuil, where the most often investigated occurrence of magnesian chalk is located, all the facies of the yellow chalk and of the magnesian chalk are associated in a very small area. The outcrop of Bimont, related to the chalk with *M.c. anguinum*, builds a small rounded hill a few hundred meters in diameter, largely opened up by abandoned and active quarries. At that place, N. de Mercey recognized in 1863 "the arrangement and the effects of a hot water spring", as well as the occurrence of "several vents of unknown depth", around which the transformations of the chalk reached their maximum intensity.

A synthetical picture of the occurrence, resulting from observations which, with the exception of one, may be verified at any time, appears as follows. The whole structure is a depression limited everywhere—bottom included—by a nodular chalk (chalk with callosities), quarried as building stone. The inside of the depression is filled, over an area not larger than 100 meters in diameter, by a complex association of yellow, very hard and massive magnesian limestone, of yellow crystalline limestone, of vuggy magnesian limestone, and of numerous nodules (*buquants*) with a crystalline or granular texture, and enclosed in ferruginous sands, called dolomitic. This association, upon close examination, has a chaotic aspect which is replaced on a large scale by a gross arrangement of the constituents into concentric depressions. Furthermore, numerous large and small cavities, oriented at random, occur throughout the mass of materials. Some of them reach 1 to 2 meters in length and .50 m in height. These cavities, which demonstrate an important reduction of volume with respect to the original chalky deposit, certainly correspond to the *vents* reported by N. de Mercey. The complex association of nodules and sands, which represent by far the major part of the structure, leaves actually only an accessory portion to the sands. These may contain, in places, enough manganese oxide to deeply stain the fingers. The nodular elements often display a shape that simulates stalactites, always in vertical position.

It is important to stress the fact that this occurrence grades in all directions, and very rapidly, into a normal white chalk; this applies also to the bottom of the depression. This last observation can only be made from time to time in relation to the progress of the quarrying operations. It was described for instance by L. Graves, in 1847, as follows: "Toward the base of the structure, the rock is continuous, massive, and usable as an ornamental stone ... The last bed is a yellow and coarse chalk ... containing rare nodules." In other words, the bottom of the depression consists of building stone grading into normal chalk. Unpublished data of P. Jodot, and my personal observations between 1890 and 1930, have several times confirmed this fact. In summary, the magnesian chalk of Bimont builds a petrographic accident, isolated within the white chalk, and devoid of any continuation at depth.

The upper part of the occurrence displays a fundamental property which has never been mentioned. It stops abruptly upwards, as if truncated, and is overlain, with a very clear *disconformity*, by white chalk, normal in all respects. *Consequently, the generation of the magnesian chalk precedes the deposition of the overlying white chalk, and in other words, corresponds to an interruption of sedimentation.*

It should be pointed out that, in the preceding occurrence, the lateral grading of the normal white chalk into magnesian products, totally different from the former, occurs over a very short distance. The same situation is illustrated elsewhere by very spectacular examples such as that of the cliff of Etretat (see footnote 42).

46. *Ibid., id.*, pp. 435-436. (see following footnote)
47. *Ibid., id.*, pp. 435-436.

I do not pretend to have demonstrated that all the occurrences of magnesian chalk of the Paris Basin are necessarily related to ruptures of equilibrium of the sea bottom, or localized along the axis of anticlines. Investigations oriented along these lines are only in an incipient stage, and may remain there for a long time yet. However, the best known and the most important occurrences may be taken into account, and used for demonstration purposes.

Regardless of what one may think of the genetic role attributed to the ruptures of equilibrium with respect to magnesian chalks, their coincidence in time and space with the formation of the above-mentioned occurrences remains an established fact. In that respect it is impossible not to be struck by the fact that *the sea affected by the magnesian accidents coincides with the portion of the Paris Basin where the ruptures of equilibrium reached their maximum frequency and amplitude*. Is not the area of the great mineralogical accidents of the chalk, at the same time, that where the folding processes display their maximum intensity? In our opinion, this is a fundamental aspect of the problem to be solved.

How can these disturbances affect the physical and chemical characters of the deposits during or after their sedimentation? Obviously, by means of slow, rapid or abrupt changes of depth, the generation of shoals, changes of pressure and temperature, intervention of new supplies, and finally by new modalities in the dynamic action of the waters. The association of these different types of modifications actually contributes to create a new generating environment, in summary, new physical, chemical and biological conditions.

If we may visualize, rather easily, the possibility of a relationship between the great submarine disturbances and the formation of magnesian accidents, the role played by the anticlines in such a concept cannot be understood at first glance.

While keeping a cautious attitude, one is naturally led to wonder if these folds did not already exist on the bottom of the Cretaceous sea, in a fashion similar to that of the submarine ridges of the area of the iron ores of Lorraine. (L. Cayeux, Les minerais de fer oolithique de France. II. Minerais de fer secondaires: *Etudes Gîtes Min. France, Min. Trav. Publics.*, 1922, p. 437). If such were the case, these folds, behaving as unstable shoals, could have generated the conditions corresponding to the above-mentioned ruptures of equilibrium. In that respect, the study of the calcium phosphates of the chalk with *Belemnitella* will demonstrate a very important fact: *the bottom of the Paris Basin already displayed anticlinal ridges at the beginning of the Campanian*.

Therefore, our line of reasoning appears hypothetical only because of the impossibility of demonstrating today that the folds related to the formation of the magnesian accidents were already outlined. But, most probably, such was the case, since they correspond to some of the most important folds of the entire Paris Basin. Besides, we can always refute the opinion, that the above-mentioned occurrences of dolomitic sands should occur along the axis of the anticlines without any genetic relationship. *Therefore, I consider the intervention of anticlinal ridges, in the process of formation or of growth, on the sea bottom, as one of the major factors in the generation of the magnesian accidents.*

This is the appropriate time to point out that the concept just presented is in perfect agreement with the idea of the repetition in time of the magnesian accidents at a given place, stressed by Ch. Barrois. For instance, in the case of an occurrence of dolomitic sands related to anticlines, if, as I have reasons to believe, the formation of these folds is a very long process, starting on the bottom of the Cretaceous sea, one can very easily conclude that the ridges, becoming accentuated at different times, could have successively generated during the Cretaceous and the Cenozic, environmental conditions favorable to the repetition of magnesian accidents.

Actually, two distinct processes operate: ruptures of equilibrium and bathymetrical changes, both resulting from submarine folding, and leading to the same environmental result, except that the second process appears particularly favorable to the generation of dolomitic sands. If I am not mistaken, both have created conditions favorable to the fixation of magnesium carbonate and to the physical changes undergone by the chalk.

48. H. LASNE, Sur les terrains phosphatés des environs de Doullens. Etage sénonien et terrains superposés: *Bull. Soc. Géol. France*, 1890, Ser. 3, vol. XVIII, pp. 472-474.

49. J. GOSSELET, Note sur les gîtes de phosphate de chaux d'Hem-Monacu, d'Etaves, du Ponthieu, etc.: *Ann. Soc. Géol. Nord*, 1896, vol. XXIV, p. 124, fig. 3.

Ibid., Note sur les gîtes phosphatés des environs de Roisel suivie des considérations générales sur les dépôts de craie phosphatée de Picardie: *Ann. Soc. Géol. Nord*, 1900, vol. XXIX, p. 76, fig. 2.

Ibid., Observations géologiques faites dans les exploitations de phosphate de chaux en 1901: *Ann. Soc. Géol. Nord*, 1901, vol. XXX, pp. 231-232, fig. 9.

50. L. CAYEUX, Phosphates sénoniens du Bassin de Paris, *in* Les Phosphates de chaux sédimentaires de France: *Etudes Gîtes Min. France, Serv. Carte Géol. France et des Top. Sout.*, 1939, vol. I, fig. 11-16, pp. 247-252 and 258-259.

Among the subdivisions of Cayeux's exhaustive description of the Senonian phosphorites of the Paris Basin (footnote 21), a section is devoted to the movements which affected the sea floor, before, during, and after the deposition of the phosphatic chalk. This question is discussed here in more detail.

H. Lasne was the first to present the idea that the phosphatic chalk of the vicinity of Doullens (Somme) had been deposited on a sea floor which had just been folded, and in close relationship with small synclinal depressions. He noticed that the phosphatic chalk displayed simultaneously its maximum thickness and highest grade always in coincidence with a synclinal depression. This double observation demonstrates that such depressions were formed before the time of deposition of the phosphatic chalk. J. Gosselet extended this observation beyond the region of Doullens recognizing the general occurrence of such folding throughout the Paris Basin. He stated that the phosphatic chalk occurred in small basins displaying the shape of ellipsoidal depressions with diameters ranging from 100 to 3000 meters.

However, the features of the chalk underlying the phosphatic varieties and the peculiar characters of the latter clearly indicate that the deformations of the sea-floor continued during the deposition of the phosphatic chalks, the high points of the sea floor acting as generating centers of the phosphatic materials and the adjacent depressions as areas where such materials were transported and accumulated.

In addition to the above-mentioned structures which involve the entire chalk formation of a given region, there are, as in the quarry of Etaves (Aisne), examples of localized folds (fig. 10, Cayeux's fig. 11) with very small radius of curvature but asymmetrical, overturned and even recumbent. In such cases, we are compelled to assume that the dislocations occurred or were strongly accentuated after the deposition of the phosphatic chalk, and before that of the overlying white chalk. Indeed, the existence of such exaggerated types of folds playing the role of basins of sedimentation on the sea floor is inconceivable because they would have been immediately and largely destroyed by the powerful action of the submarine currents which play such an important role in the deposition of the phosphatic chalks.

Also in the case of the quarry of Etaves, it may be shown that the folding of the phosphatic chalk which preceded the deposition of the overlying white one, was again accentuated later, since that chalk displays a slight inflexion corre-

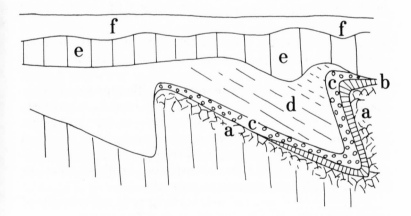

Fig. 10. Folding of the phosphatic chalk at Etaves (Aisne).
    a. Perforated surface of the white chalk with *M.c. anguinum.*
    b. Indurated chalk.
    c. Phosphatic conglomerate.
    d. Phosphatic chalk with *B. quadrata.*
    e. White chalk with *B. quadrata.*
    f. *Limon.*

(After J. Gosselet, *op. cit.,* p. 124)

sponding to one of the underlying synclines. J. Gosselet considered that this new phase of folding took place during the beginning of the deposition of the white chalk since its upper part displays no trace of it.

With respect to these different types of folds, J. Gosselet used the terms of "tectonic" and even "orogenic movements". Actually, all these accidents, large and small, are related to the foldings with large radius of curvature which affected the chalk of the entire Paris Basin, and as such they do not have an orogenic character.

In conclusion, it should be pointed out that the phosphatic chalks represent a perfect demonstration of the effects of long-lasting phases of deformation contemporaneous with sedimentation. Similar conditions are displayed by the magnesian chalks of the Paris Basin (footnote 45) and by the occurrence of the cherts in the chalk of the same region (footnote 21). If we also consider the Mesozoic oolitic iron ores of Lorraine, the processes of deformation contemporaneous with sedimentation acquire a fundamental importance in numerous environments of deposition of the geological past.

51. L. CAYEUX, *op. cit.*, pp. 249-252, fig. 14-16. *Angular unconformity of the phosphatic chalk on the chalk with M.C. ANGUINUM.*

The phosphatic chalk overlies either the chalk with *M.c. anguinum*, whose mineral and organic composition has been deeply modified, or the typical chalk with *M.c. anguinum* devoid of its upper modified portion. In the most common case, where erosion has destroyed the upper part of the chalk with *M.c. anguinum*, the phosphatic chalk overlies its substratum with an angular unconformity.

The latter may be extremely striking as in the example of Curlu (Somme) described by H. Lasne. The section (fig. 11, Cayeux's fig. 14) shows the basal conglomerate of the phosphatic chalk forming an arch and cutting the essentially horizontal beds of the white chalk in a wedge-like manner. The author interpreted this situation as resulting from "mechanical erosion" and particularly from "chemical

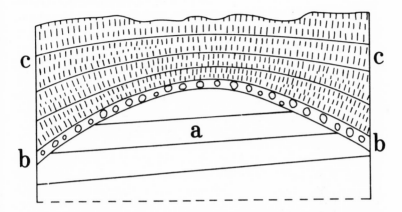

Fig. 11. Angular unconformity of the phosphatic chalk with *B. quadrata* on the white chalk with *M.c. anguinum*, near Curlu (Somme).
   a. White chalk with *M.c. anguinum*.
   b. Nodular bed at the base of the phosphatic chalk.
   c. Phosphatic chalk with *B. quadrata*.
(After H. Lasne, *op. cit.*, p. 228)

erosion". However, it should be related to the erosional phase which marks the beginning of the Campanian; in other words, this angular unconformity is only the local expression of a very general phenomenon.

Transgression of the phosphatic chalk

H. Lasne having noticed the wedging out of beds of phosphatic chalk concluded that phenomena of transgression and regression occurred among such deposits.

The existence of a relatively large-scale transgression has been clearly demonstrated in the deposit of Templeux-le-Guérard (Somme). J. Gosselet observed a depression preceding the deposition of the phosphatic chalk, although he could not ascertain whether it was of tectonic origin or due to an important process of erosion (fig. 12, Cayeux's fig. 15). Within that depression, the bottom of which is entirely lined with a phosphatic conglomerate, different types of phosphatic chalks have been deposited on the two flanks of the depression. On one side they are regularly superposed, on the

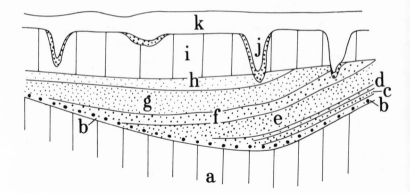

Fig. 12. Transgressive stratification of the phosphatic formation at
        Templeux-le-Guérard (Somme).
        a. White chalk.
        b. Conglomerate with small phosphatic nodules (0.15 m).
        c. Phosphatic chalk with 37% calcium phosphate (1.50 m).
        d. Bed of small phosphatic nodules (0.12 m).
        e. Phosphatic chalk of same type as "c" (2.00 m).
        f. Low grade phosphatic chalk (1.80 m).
        g. Phosphatic chalk with 40% calcium phosphate (3.50 m).
        h. Phosphatic chalk with 13 to 20% calcium phosphate (3.00
           m).
        i. Upper white chalk.
        j. Pockets containing phosphatic sand.
        k. *Limon* and Cenozoic formation.
                                (After J. Gosselet, *op. cit.* p. 76)

other they overlap one another in a transgressive manner. All
these deposits are overlain unconformably by the white chalk
which is clearly transgressive, a situation recalling that of the
quarry of Etaves (see footnote 50, fig. 10, Cayeux's fig. 11).

In the region of Beauval, H. Lasne has observed another
very localized example of angular unconformity showing a
small depression of phosphatic chalk, faulted in the middle,
truncated at the top and overlain by horizontally stratified
white chalk with *B. quadrata* (fig. 13, Cayeux's fig. 16).

*Relationships between the phosphatic chalk and its cover of
white chalk with B. QUADRATA.*

The section described by J. Gosselet at Etaves (fig. 10,
Cayeux's fig. 11) certainly demonstrates that the formation
of the two asymmetrical folds preceded the deposition of the

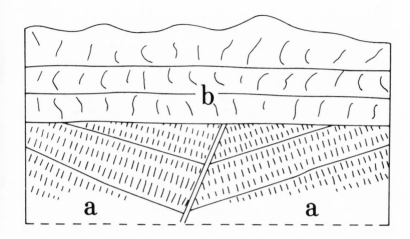

Fig. 13. Angular unconformity of the white chalk with *B. quadrata* on the phosphatic chalk with *B. quadrata* near Beauval.
a. Phosphatic chalk with *B. quadrata*.
b. White chalk with *B. quadrata*.

(After H. Lasne, *op. cit.*, p. 230)

upper white chalk. This section not only shows a spectacular angular unconformity between the white chalk and the underlying phosphatic chalk, but also displays, in the southwestern part of the quarry, this same white chalk overlying directly either the basal conglomerate, or the cemented substratum, which belong to the chalk with *M.c. anguinum*.

The section of the quarry of Templeux-le-Guérard, described by J. Gosselet (fig. 12, Cayeux's fig. 15) displays, as clearly as at Etaves, angular unconformity and transgression. The white chalk with *B. quadrata* may be seen truncating in succession several beds of the phosphatic chalk which fills the depression.

52. L. CAYEUX, Les roches sédimentaires de France. Roches siliceuses: *Mém. Carte géol. France*, 1929, p. 586, fig. 14. See footnote 21.

53. *Ibid.*, *id.*, p. 585, fig. 11-13. See footnote 21.

54. L. CAYEUX, Les minerais de fer oolithique de France. II. Minerais de fer secondaires: *Etudes Gîtes Min. France, Min. Trav. Publics.*, 1922, pp. 436-437, 934.

The generation of the oolitic iron ores of Lorraine always implies the existence of two environments, the first in which the ferruginous materials are generated, the second where they are concentrated. The analysis of the fragments of reworked ores reveals that the generating environment is located either shoreward, or in the direction of the open sea, and sometimes quite near the area of concentration of the constituents.

The frequency of the debris brought in from the open sea requires either the constant existence of shoals whose deposits are continuously reworked, or of areas tending toward emergence or at least brought close to sea level. In order to explain the generation of a large portion of the reworked materials, folds or ridges should be visualized which allowed the ore to be reworked immediately after its formation, mainly from the time of deposition of the middle band of ores until the end of the period favorable to the generation of the ore. Furthermore, these folds must have been immediately rebuilt after being destroyed, in order to develop the conditions necessary for a continuous reworking. In addition, the existence of emerged and permanent ridges cannot be considered, since among the reworked materials of a given layer none are derived from an older deposit. We are therefore gradually led to the two following concepts: 1. folding contemporaneous with the deposition of the ores; 2. occurrence of areas undergoing littoral and sublittoral conditions in the midst of the open sea during most of the time corresponding to the formation of the ores of Lorraine.

55. SIR JOHN MURRAY, *The depths of the ocean*: a general account of the modern science of oceanography based largely on the scientific researches of the Norwegian steamer Michael Sars in the North Atlantic by Sir John Murray . . . and Dr. Johan Hjort, with contributions from Professor A. Appellöf, Prof. H.H. Gran and Dr. B. Helland-Hansen: 1912, London, Macmillan and

Co. Ltd., p. 189: "Deep-sea conditions are, on the whole, more favorable to the degradation of mineral matter than to the generation of new minerals. Nevertheless, a few syntheses are being continuously carried on in the immediately superjacent layers of water; they fall into two groups, viz. true chemical syntheses of new classes of silicates, and mineralogical syntheses of concretionary minerals. The first group comprises glauconite and phillipsite; the second group, ferromanganic and phosphate concretions."

56. In my opinion, it would have been better to establish for the abyssal red clay a particular class of chemical deposits, distinct from the group of typical sediments.

57. The absence of phosphatic concretions in present-day pelagic oozes is not absolute, because J. Murray and A.F. Renard have illustrated thin sections from concretions dredged in the *Globigerina* ooze of the Indian Ocean at a depth of 1,900 fathoms (3,480 meters). The "Challenger" has also reported some of them, at the same depth in the *Globigerina* ooze, south of the Agulhas Bank. In all similar cases, we are dealing with accidental features as may be observed in very rare instances in the purest chalks of the Paris Basin, developed under the influence of concretionary processes completely unrelated with the phosphatic sedimentation (J. Murray and A.F. Renard, *op. cit.*, pl. XX, fig. 3 and 4). [For a discussion of Recent marine phosphorites, see Editor's Introduction.]

58. L. CAYEUX, Les phosphates de chaux sédimentaires de France: *Etudes Gîtes Min. France. Serv. de la Carte Géol. France et des Top. Sout.*, 1939, vol. I, p. 81. See footnote 40.

59. The investigation of the oolitic iron ores of Lorraine has led me to assume in a number of deposits the generation of *quartz* on the sea floor.

60. L. CAYEUX, Les ressources minérales de la France d'Outre-Mer. IV. Le Phosphate: *Publ. bureau d'études géologiques et minières coloniales*, 1935, Paris, Soc. Edit.

Géogr. Marit. et Coloniales. Les phosphates de chaux
sédimentaires. Manières d'être et mode de formation, pp.
11-14.

Since the discovery of bony debris in the phosphatic
chalks of Belgium and France by A.F. Renard and J. Cornet,
and also because the exploitation of large deposits yielded
numerous microscopic remains of fish and saurians, organisms and fish in particular have been considered as the
principal agent of fixation and concentration of the phosphoric acid.

Fish, however, did not exist at the time of generation of
the oldest phosphorites; therefore, their participation is not
absolutely necessary. Furthermore, their debris in the thin
sections of Paleozoic phosphates are, on the average, extremely rare, if not absent. For instance, they are completely
missing in the Dinantian phosphorites of the Pyrenees and
the Montagne-Noire. This rarity of occurrence continues to
be the rule until the Albian included. Afterwards, the
frequency of fish debris greatly increases, reaching its
maximum during the Senonian and the lower Eocene, when
they become an important constituent. At present, their
contribution to the composition of the most recent phosphates, such as those of the Agulhas Bank, is practically nil.

By assuming that the fish have really played the role
usually attributed to them, the greatly variable frequency of
their debris represents a serious objection. Of course, it seems
natural that their representatives would be scarce, rare or
very rare, in the deposits to which they provided phosphoric
acid, but it is inconceivable that they should occur with great
abundance in the most important accumulations of phosphate. In general, the larger the phosphatic formation, the
rarer the fish remains, since they constitute the very source
of the phosphoric acid. Actually, just the opposite situation
is the rule in the great deposits of North Africa.

The following objection is of even more fundamental
nature. During the formation of the North-African deposits,
an enormous amount of fish remains would have been
destroyed on the sea floor, through an unknown process, in

order to produce the phosphoric acid of the grains. Simultaneously, a very large proportion of the debris would have had the chance to escape destruction and to remain intact. I really mean intact, because these debris appear as fragments, shards and splinters with sharp edges which are perfectly preserved. Furthermore, I insist on the fact that these debris are devoid of any trace of corrosion. That materials of same composition should display such completely opposed behaviors within the same sedimentary environment, is to me an undecipherable enigma.

I am inclined now to believe that the great distribution and the abundance of fish remains in the phosphate deposits of Morocco, Algeria, Tunisia, the Paris Basin, etc., are due only to environmental conditions favorable to the concentration of phosphoric acid from which the fish themselves took advantage. In other words: *fish remains are abundant because, under influences which remain to be defined, certain submarine bottoms provided them with an exceptional supply of phosphoric acid.* Therefore, our problem appears completely changed with respect to one of its fundamental data, since the cause becomes the effect . . .

As soon as I began to entertain doubts about the active role attributed to the fish, I have oriented my investigations in the direction of bacterial activity. I have therefore searched for bacteria in sedimentary phosphorites, and my investigations were not unsuccessful. At present, I know numerous bacteria only in two types of phosphates. Since I would like to remain on the solid ground of facts, I shall not generalize and state that all sedimentary phosphorites are of bacterial origin.

But, let us assume for a moment that the number of positive data is bound to increase. Following such a hypothesis, I assume that we would reach the following formula: *The ruptures of equilibrium of the sea floor which precede the formation of the deposits, unlatch a great bacterial activity which until that time was dormant. This activity generates phosphoric acid at the expense of sea water and, consequently, forms calcium phosphate in the presence of calcium carbonate. Simultaneously, the fish,* to speak only of the major marine organisms using phosphorus, *having at their disposal an important source of phosphoric acid, become unusually abundant, and their debris, incorporated in the sediments, contribute to a variable extent, to the formation of the deposits.*

Let us consider all this, for the time being, as a working hypothesis, and as a promising new concept for understanding the processes of formation of sedimentary phosphorites.

L. CAYEUX, Existence de nombreuses Bactéries dans les phosphates sedimentaires de tout âge: Conséquences: *C.R. Acad. Sc. Paris*, 1936, vol. 203, pp. 1198-1200.

The inadequacy of the different theories proposed to explain the formation of sedimentary phosphorites was bound sooner or later to orient the investigations in the direction of bacterial actions. Bacteria were indeed discovered in 1933, and described the following year, in materials from two different deposits (see previous reference). However, these Bacteria were very difficult to observe, and good photographs demonstrating their existence hard to obtain. Besides, the question remained open whether the two investigated deposits represented exceptions or not.

In the hope of obtaining clear pictures of these Bacteria I used infrared photography which not only confirmed my first identifications, but also led to the discovery of Bacteria within phosphates of greatly variable age.

Indeed, I have recognized their occurrence in the phosphates of the Agulhas Bank, dredged south of the Cape of Good Hope (see footnote 16). They also occur in great abundance in the phosphates of North Africa which span the Cretaceous-Cenozoic boundary; in the Campanian phosphatic chalks, exploited on a large scale in the past in northern France; as well as in the nodular phosphates of the Turonian, Cenomanian, Albian, Portlandian and Liassic of the Paris Basin.

The Paleozoic phosphorites contain less Bacteria than the preceding ones. Their occurrence has been recognized in the

Permian phosphates of the Rocky Mountains, in the Dinantian phosphates of the Pyrenees, in the Devonian phosphates of Tennessee, in the Ordovician phosphates of Wales, and finally—in very small number—in the Lower Cambrian phosphates of Sweden.

Actually, I have found Bacteria in all the phosphatic materials where I have looked for them. In conclusion, one can say that *Bacteria occur in phosphates throughout the geological column.*

In general, these organisms appear as spherules provided with a very thick envelope, and ranging in diameter from .5 to 2.5 microns. They may be observed most frequently as isolated bodies, but also occur arranged in straight rows, or associated in small irregularly-shaped masses. In order to give an idea of their frequency in a thin section of phosphate from Kourigha (Morocco), where they are abundant, several hundreds of them may be counted at a magnification of X 800 over a field of one hundredth and a half of a square millimeter, excluding all those which are not located exactly in the focusing plane. Their abundance may be even greater in other instances, but it is far from being true in all the investigated cases. Furthermore, adjacent areas within the same thin section may show large variations of frequency.

As previously reported, I have reached the concept that Bacteria produce calcium phosphate at the expense of sea water, whose supply of phosphoric acid is constantly renewed through influx by rivers. The role of fish and marine reptiles in the generation of phosphatic deposits has been greatly exaggerated, if not misunderstood. Their remains are abundant because they found over the areas of the sea floor where calcium phosphate was accumulating through a biochemical process, an exceptional supply of phosphoric acid which allowed them to multiply under abnormal conditions, and not at all—as usually believed—because they have been themselves the generating agents of the deposits.

In the present state of our knowledge, processes belonging to mineral or inorganic chemistry are generally proposed to explain the origin of many sedimentary rocks such as

limestones, dolomites, siliceous rocks, phosphorites, etc.
However, we have known for many years, that the large
group of the combustible rocks, escape this general rule since
they result from the transformation of vegetable remains
under the influence of bacterial agents. Now, we are certain
that sedimentary phosphorites, also of biochemical origin,
represent a second exception. It remains to be seen if the
exception shall not become the general rule in time, and
whether with increasing knowledge the reactions which
regulate the generation of other categories of sedimentary
rocks will not also belong to biochemistry.

61. I would like to add, although it may not seem pertinent
to my subject, how desirable it would be to give a more
geological character to oceanographic investigations. For
instance, the example of the phosphates of the Agulhas
Bank which were shown to be very old by a microscopic
study, is sufficient by itself to justify such an opinion.

[Cayeux's wish has been fulfilled since the program of the
Deep Sea Drilling Project is indeed entirely conducted for
geological purposes. Among its major aims are the checking
of the hypotheses of continental drift and sea floor spreading
as well as a determination of the age of the major ocean
basins.]

LIST OF ILLUSTRATIONS

INDEX